THE LANCASHIRE CRICKET QUIZ BOOK

MALCOLM LORIMER &
BOB WARBURTON

First published in Great Britain in 1989 by
MAINSTREAM PUBLISHING COMPANY (EDINBURGH) LTD
7 Albany Street, Edinburgh EH1 3UG

ISBN 1 85158 270 3 (paper)

British Library Cataloguing in Publication Data
Lorimer, Malcolm
The Lancashire cricket quiz book.
1. Lancashire. County cricket. Clubs.
Lancashire County Cricket Club, to 1988
I. Title
796.35'863'094276

ISBN 1-85158-270-3

Cover photograph of Old Trafford Cricket Ground by Adrian Murrell

Typeset in 11 on 13pt Imprint by Bookworm Typesetting, Edinburgh
Printed in Great Britain by Billings & Sons, Worcester.

This book is dedicated to all the cricketers whose achievements have made it possible.

Contents

Acknowledgements

When was the last time . . .? Who was the last . . .? On which ground did . . .? Has a Lancashire player ever . . .?

There seems to be an inexhaustible supply of questions concerning cricket which fascinate or intrigue, and many and varied they are. This book of 1,000 questions on Lancashire cricket and cricketers reflects something of the interest shown in this great game and how fascinating it can be. As compilers of the Lancashire yearbook we seem to be asked many of the rather more obscure questions that appear in this book. We hope that it will answer some of those questions as well as amuse and inform the readers about Lancashire cricket and cricketers. The questions range from the trivial, 'Did Dora Bryan's husband really play for Lancashire?' to the obscure, 'Who is remembered in the Old Trafford Museum by a red serviette?'

We would like to thank Brian Bearshaw, cricket writer and journalist, for supplying the foreword, Charles Oliver for his kind assistance in checking through our questions and answers. Also thanks to Raye Dobson for managing to read our writing and typing the copy, the staff of Lancashire C.C.C. for their assistance and redirecting any people who come with obscure cricket questions!

We would like to thank all those members who come into the club shop or the Library and ask . . . When was . . .? Who was the . . .? On which ground . . . etc . . . etc . . . etc.!

We hope that you enjoy the book as much as we have enjoyed putting it together.

Bob Warburton
(Assistant Secretary Lancashire C.C.C.)

Rev. Malcolm G. Lorimer
(Hon. Librarian and Statistician Lancashire C.C.C.)

Foreword

For somebody like me, up to my eyeballs in researching and writing the Official History of Lancashire County Cricket Club, such a mountain of questions and answers contained in these pages is invaluable.

So many of the major points of the history are in this book. Anything worth recording is here. Anybody who is anybody is mentioned, although considering his relatively few matches (46) for Lancashire, it speaks volumes for the reputation of Sydney Barnes that he gets more than his fair share of appearances in the book.

No outstanding player is overlooked, and readers might find it interesting to use this book from which to find their outstanding Lancashire team of all time.

My own occasionally changes. I learn something more about a particular individual and feel feel rather strongly that he is a player I would like to have seen.

Vernon Royle is a case in point. The reverend gentleman was regarded as the finest cover point fielder in England in the last century. His batting, judging by his figures, was fairly ordinary, but his fielding was in a class of its own, and they say he was worth his place in a team for that alone. I would love to have seen him in action, yet I doubt really whether he was good enough to command a place in the greatest team through Lancashire's 125-year history.

A.G. Steel is another player I find hard to come to terms with. He played only one match more than Barnes for Lancashire and too often chose to play in grander, showier matches of the time than for his county. But he was a true Lancastrian, played for no other county, and was regarded for many years as second only to W.G. Grace as the country's outstanding all-round cricketer, a marvellous batsman and a remarkable spin-bowler. All things considered he has to go into my team.

My first four batsmen are all Lancastrians and I have no doubts as to their credentials . . . Archie MacLaren, Cyril Washbrook,

J.T. Tyldesley and his brother Ernest. The two quick-bowlers are easy to select – Ted McDonald and Brian Statham – and my spinners are Johnny Briggs and Roy Tattersall, although I am sorry I cannot find a place for another Tyldesley, leg-spinner Dick.

I would choose Dick Pilling, from the early days of Lancashire cricket, ahead of George Duckworth and Farokh Engineer as wicket-keeper, and though I badly want Cec Parkin for the remaining place in the team, I go for Clive Lloyd to achieve balance, and provide me with the player who has given me the greatest enjoyment through the years.

So there we are: MacLaren, Washbrook, J.T. Tyldesley, Ernest Tyldesley, Lloyd, Steel, Briggs, Pilling, McDonald, Statham and Tattersall.

When you have gone through this book, you will come up with your own favourites, your own outstanding team. Lancashire is rich in history, in outstanding players and events, and Bob and Malcolm have missed nothing along the way.

When I was asked go write the foreword I was told I would probably answer 90 per cent of the questions correctly. It was nearer 60 per cent in the end, and then I thought I had done well.

The questions are testing and teasing. I wish you the best of luck.

Brian Bearshaw
Cricket Writer and Journalist
December 1988

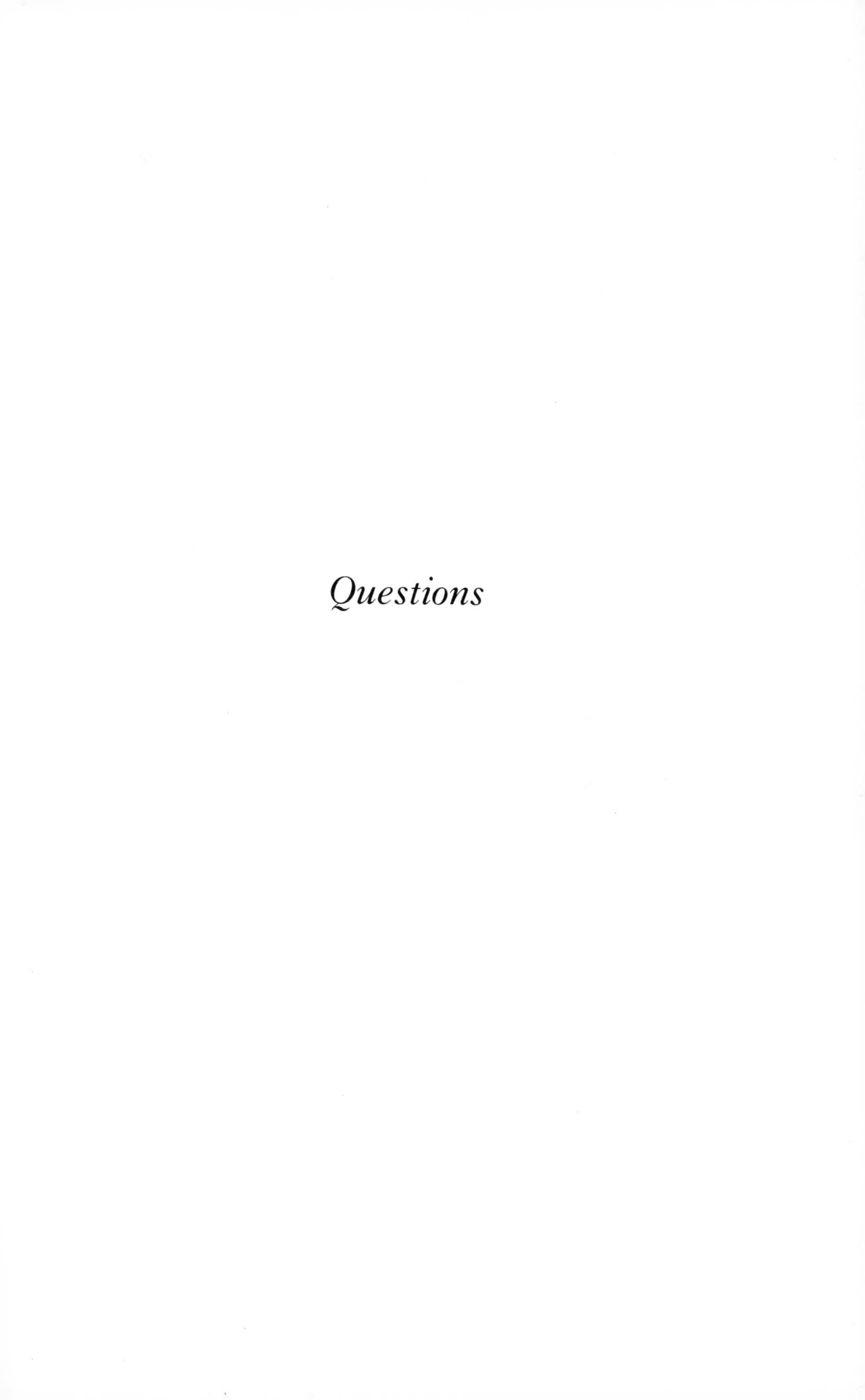

Questions

LANCASHIRE IN THE COUNTY CHAMPIONSHIP

1 When did Lancashire win the County Championship three years in succession?

2 Against whom was Lancashire's lowest score of 25 all out in the County Championship?

3 Against which club did Lancashire establish their record score, and how many did they score?

4 When was the last time Lancashire shared the County Championship?

5 With whom did they share the Championship?

6 Lancashire have beaten one team four times inside a day in first-class matches; which team is it?

7 When did Lancashire last tie a County Championship match?

8 The only first-class cricket match in England when a side won and didn't lose a wicket in either innings happened in June 1956. Who did Lancashire beat?

9 Have Lancashire ever finished bottom of the County Championship and if so in which year?

10 When did Lancashire last go through a season and not lose a match in the County Championship?

LANCASHIRE IN THE COUNTY CHAMPIONSHIP – 2

11 In which year did Lancashire win both the first-class and Minor County competitions?

12 Which two Lancashire bowlers took all 20 Sussex wickets in the match which ended on the first day?

13 Who carried his bat for 125 through a Lancashire innings of 197 at The Oval in 1951?

14 In 1911 Lancashire won by an innings and 455 runs. Who were they playing and where?

15 Who scored a century against the Argentine in Belgrano?

16 Who scored three hundreds against Hampshire in two years?

17 Who on his debut in 1866, took six for 30 against Surrey?

18 Which team were all out for 37 against Lancashire in two successive seasons?

19 Lancashire beat Somerset at Bath in one day in 1955. Whose Benefit match was it?

20 Who was the last Lancashire player to take 100 wickets in a season?

OLD TRAFFORD

21 In what year was Lancashire's first county match at Old Trafford?

22 Who was the last player to take a hat-trick for Lancashire at Old Trafford?

23 Which Lancashire player has made the highest score for Lancashire at Old Trafford?

24 Which four Lancashire players are the office blocks next to the ground named after?

25 Which other two Lancashire cricketers are remembered by roads named after them near the ground?

26 Which member of the Royal Family attended the last day of the Test Match against New Zealand in 1949?

27 What was Old Trafford's pavilion used for during the First World War?

28 Who was the first batsman to hit a ball right out of the ground from a wicket pitched in the middle?

29 Who went 'shooting pigeons' on the ground with his friends in the early years?

30 Who took the first hat-trick for Lancashire at Old Trafford?

LANCASHIRE GROUNDS – AIGBURTH, LIVERPOOL

31 In which year did the Aigburth ground stage its first County match?

32 Who scored 248 for Lancashire against Worcestershire in 1903 at Aigburth?

PICTURE QUIZ – 1

He played in 1939 and had the same name as a more famous player.

33 Which team bowled Lancashire out for 37 in 1907 at Aigburth?

34 Who took 11 wickets for Cambridge University in the first match at Aigburth?

35 Who bowled Bradman in the Tourist match in 1930?

36 Who took 14 for 99 against Leicestershire in his first match for Lancashire at Aigburth?

37 In 1913 Harry Dean took 17 for 91 at Aigburth. Against whom?

38 Which player scored 366 runs in four days' cricket at Aigburth and Old Trafford in 1983?

39 Who bowled Lancashire out for 49 but then were bowled out themselves for 22, and what was the year?

40 Who played Lancashire in a 12-a-side one-day match at Fazakerley in 1941?

LANCASHIRE GROUNDS – BLACKPOOL

41 Who scored a double century against the Indian tourists in 1959 at Blackpool?

42 Who hit 17 sixes in a match against Lancashire at Blackpool?

43 In which year did Lancashire first play a first-class match at Blackpool?

44 Which Australian scored 150 in one hour 55 minutes in 1909 at Blackpool against an England XI?

45 Who piloted a two-seater aircraft from Manchester to Blackpool to take part in a County match in 1929?

46 Which team did Lancashire play in the Sunday League in 1976 at Blackpool?

47 Which two Lancashire batsmen shared an opening stand of 146 in this match?

48 Who donated the ground to Blackpool C.C. in 1923?

49 Who took ten for 102 for Lancashire in 1953 at Blackpool?

50 Against whom?

LANCASHIRE GROUNDS – SOUTHPORT

51 When did Lancashire first play at Southport and who were their opponents?
52 For which beneficiary was a match staged against Oxford University at Southport?
53 Who opened the new pavilion in July 1965?
54 Who did Lancashire play in the televised Sunday League match at Southport in 1969?
55 Who scored 100 in each innings of the match against Worcestershire in 1979?

LANCASHIRE v. WARWICKSHIRE, SOUTHPORT 1982

56 Which two Warwickshire players scored double centuries in this match?
57 For which wicket did they share a record partnership of 470?
58 Which Warwickshire player fielded as substitute, bowled and took a wicket?
59 Which two Lancashire players made career best performances in the match?
60 How many wickets did Lancashire win by?

OTHER LANCASHIRE GROUNDS

61 Where is the most recent ground on which first-class cricket has been played and in what year?
62 Have Lancashire ever played first-class cricket at Lancaster?
63 When did Lancashire last play at Blackburn in a first-class fixture?
64 On how many grounds in Lancashire have the County played first-class cricket since the Second World War?
65 Why were Nelson given a first-class fixture by Lancashire in 1925?

LANCASHIRE v. YORKSHIRE

66 How many wickets fell on the last day of the Roses match at Headingley in 1987?

67 In whose honour was a match played between Lancashire and Yorkshire in 1913 at Liverpool?

68 Who is the last Lancashire player to score centuries in both Roses matches in the same season?

69 Lancashire played Yorkshire on this ground in Lancashire in 1867 and it was the only time first-class cricket has been played there. Where is it?

70 What is Lancashire's lowest total against Yorkshire?

71 Who chose a Roses match for his Benefit match and there was not a ball bowled?

72 Which Lancashire player took 74 minutes before scoring in a Roses match at Sheffield in 1969?

73 Who has scored most centuries for Lancashire in Roses matches?

74 Whose only century in first-class cricket was against Yorkshire?

75 In 1978, who scored 51 in 34 balls at Headingley?

LANCASHIRE v. YORKSHIRE

76 Who, in the same season, played for Lancashire and then captained Yorkshire in a Roses match?

77 Who has made the only double century for Lancashire in the Roses matches?

78 Where was a Roses match staged during 1915 with equipment sent by Lancashire?

79 Yorkshire required 57 to win with a whole day to get the runs in 1924. How many did they score?

80 Who took a wicket with his first ball in County cricket which was in a Roses match?

81 Who scored the first century for Lancashire in the Roses matches?

82 When did Lancashire last beat Yorkshire twice in the same season?

83 Who was the clergyman who took four wickets for no runs at Sheffield in 1888 for Lancashire?

84 Who took 125 wickets in 14 Roses matches, commencing in 1903?

85 In 1920 at Bradford, Harry Dean took 11 for 113 in the match. Which Yorkshire bowler took nine second innings wickets for 36?

86 Name any of the four players who have played for both counties in these fixtures.

87 Who scored a double century for Yorkshire at Old Trafford in 1949?

88 What record for Roses matches did the Yorkshire openers Hutton and Watson set in 1947 at Old Trafford?

89 What event was commemorated in 1949 in Sheffield?

90 Which Lancashire player carried his bat for 152 out of 305 at Old Trafford in 1924?

PICTURE QUIZ – 2

Who is being caught?

EARLY DAYS

91 What was the official name of the County club between 1880 and 1957?

92 Why did Lord Harris of Kent refuse to play Lancashire in 1885?

93 Which county did Lancashire play in their first County Championship match and in which year?

94 Which two Lancashire players were chosen to play for R.A. Fitzgerald's tour to Canada and America in 1872?

95 Who took 9-53 for the Australians against Lancashire in 1878?

96 When did Lancashire first win the County Championship outright?

97 Which early Lancashire cricketer also had a shop in Stretford Road?

98 Who were the four Lancashire players who played in the first Old Trafford Test Match against Australia in 1884?

99 Who was the fifth player who would have played had he not been injured?

100 Which Lancashire player was one of Wisden's 'Six Great Bowlers of the Year' in 1889?

1880-1900

101 Who was the first player to score 1,000 runs in a season for Lancashire?

102 Who was selected as one of Wisden's 'Five Great Bowlers' in 1892?

103 Which left arm spinner opened the bowling for Lancashire in the Roses match at Old Trafford in 1891?

104 Which two Lancashire batsmen added 111 for the last wicket against Leicestershire in 1895?

105 Who in 1898 recorded the highest ever individual innings against Lancashire?

106 What relation was the Treasurer of Lancashire to the Captain in 1894?

107 Who had a Benefit in the 1890s when 24,000 people came on the first day but play was not possible on the other days?

108 Who played against Lancashire for Sussex in 1894 at the age of 51 and bowled 52 overs?

109 Who was Captain of Harrow and in his first innings in first-class cricket scored 108 for Lancashire?

110 Who in 1897 at The Oval bowled Lohmann and sent a bail 63 yards six inches?

1890s

111 Which two Lancashire bowlers bowled unchanged through a match at Old Trafford against Sussex in 1890 taking 19 wickets?

112 In Lancashire's record score of 801, who else scored a century besides MacLaren's 424?

113 Who took 13 Somerset wickets in 1894 in the match which was completed in one day?

114 Why was A.C. MacLaren absent for eight matches prior to the Somerset match at Taunton in 1895?

115 Which two Lancashire bowlers claimed 326 wickets out of the 387 wickets captured by Lancashire in 1894?

A. C. MACLAREN'S 424

116 Whose record did A.C. MacLaren beat when he scored 424?

117 Who was the Australian-born all-rounder who captained Somerset in this match?

118 Who put on 363 with MacLaren for the second wicket?

119 Who beat this score in 1923?

120 How many boundaries did he hit in his record innings?

THE GOLDEN AGE

121 Which great Lancashire bowler made his debut for the County in 1902?

122 Which two sides did Lancashire score over 600 against in 1905?

123 Which County was dismissed for 65 at Old Trafford in 1905 when Lancashire went on to score 424 for eight at the close of the first day?

124 Who in 1902 came on as a substitute for Sydney Barnes and later on batted in the match?

125 Who retired in 1908 from the County Club after 48 years association with the Club?

126 In 1910 at Old Trafford what caused the match v. Kent to be limited to two days?

127 Who scored more runs than anyone else in England in 1910 and also came top of the first-class batting averages?

128 What was remarkable about Lancashire's win against Notts at Old Trafford in 1910?

129 What unusual occurence took place in the match against Kent at Maidstone in 1913?

130 Who was left out of the team for the match 'The Champion County v. The Rest' in 1904, offered his resignation, but later on withdrew his request?

THE GOLDEN AGE – 1900s

131 Which famous Lancashire cricketer died on 11 January 1902?

132 Who dismissed Victor Trumper six times in 1905?

133 Which player made his debut in 1906 commencing an association with the club that was to last 45 years?

134 Who bowled Lancashire out for 44 in 1901?

135 Which England player scored 170* and 204 against Lancashire in 1901?

136 Who bowled for Lancashire for the last time at Lords in 1901?

137 Who took 131 wickets in Championship matches for Lancashire in 1903?

138 Who was the umpire who no-balled Arthur Mold 18 times for throwing in the match at Old Trafford against Somerset in 1901?

139 Who made his debut for Lancashire in 1909 scoring 61?

140 Who played for the Gentlemen v. Players in 1907 taking all ten of the Players' wickets?

PICTURE QUIZ – 3

1948 Test. Barnes is injured but who hit the ball?

AFTER THE FIRST WORLD WAR

141 Who captained Lancashire immediately after the First World War?

142 In 1920, Hampshire were set 66 to win at Liverpool. What was the result?

143 Who took six catches in an innings in 1921 to set a new fielding record for Lancashire?

144 Who scored two centuries in the match against Essex at Leyton in 1921?

145 In 1921, who carried his bat through an innings on two occasions?

146 Which county recorded their first ever win against Lancashire in 1922?

147 Who became the third Lancashire player to score 2,000 runs in a season for the County?

148 Whose untimely death in 1923 meant that Lancashire were virtually without a fast bowler that year?

149 On the first day of a match in 1923 Lancashire scored 332 and reduced the opposition to 88 for nine by the close of play. Who were they playing?

150 Who scored 330 together for the third wicket against Lancashire at Old Trafford in 1925?

BETWEEN THE WARS – 1920s

151 Who scored 272 for Lancashire at Chesterfield against Derbyshire in 1919 aged 45?

152 Which former Lancashire player stood as an umpire in 1919 and died in the same year?

153 Who made two double hundreds in 1923 for Lancashire?

154 Who carried his bat twice through an innings in 1925?

155 Who made his last appearance for Lancashire in the Roses match in 1923 at Old Trafford when he captained the side?

THREE CHAMPIONSHIPS IN THREE YEARS 1926

156 How many consecutive scores of 50 or more did Ernest Tyldesley make in first-class cricket?

157 Who equalled the record in 1946-47?

158 Who shared a partnership of 279 against Notts to help win the Championship at Old Trafford?

159 Who took 11 wickets in the match?
160 Who scored 172 against Lancashire for 'The Rest' against the Champion County at the Oval?

1927

161 On which ground did C. Hallows and F. Watson put on 260 for the first wicket against Hampshire?
162 Who did Lancashire pip for the Championship?
163 Which young future England player scored 99 and 187 at Old Trafford against Lancashire?
164 Who took 150 wickets for Lancashire?
165 Lancashire only lost one game. Against whom?

1928

166 How many defeats did Lancashire suffer in 1928 in the County Championship?
167 Which two batsmen made scores of over 250 in Charlie Hallows' Benefit match?
168 Who set a record partnership for Lancashire in this match?
169 Who were the three batsmen who each scored 2,000 runs in the season?
170 Who played in a friendly match at Blackpool for Wales and took six wickets at the age of 55?
171 Who scored nine centuries for Lancashire?
172 Which Lancashire player was chosen as one of Wisden's 'Cricketers of the Year'?
173 How many catches and stumpings did he make during the season?
174 What was significant about Charlie Hallows' 232?
175 Who scored 242 at Leicester for Lancashire?

THE 1930s

176 Which two Lancashire players were chosen to go to Australia for the 1932-33 Test series?

177 In which years did Len Hopwood do the 'double' of 1,000 runs and 100 wickets?

178 What position did Lancashire finish in the County Championship in 1929 after their three successive Championships?

179 Which side (who won the Championship) did Lancashire beat by an innings in 1932?

180 Who scored 152 for Lancashire in the match?

181 Who was the Lancashire player to take 131 wickets in the 1932 season?

182 What two records for the County did Ernest Tyldesley set in 1934?

183 Who carried his bat through both innings for India at Aigburth in 1936?

184 Who dismissed Lancashire for 45 at Preston in 1936?

185 Which 18-year-old professional made his debut for Lancashire in 1933?

186 Who took all ten Lancashire wickets at Old Trafford in 1931?

187 Who put on 278 for the sixth wicket with Jack Iddon in 1932 at Old Trafford against Sussex?

188 Who scored a century in George Duckworth's Benefit match in 1934, his last first-class century?

189 Where did Ernest Tyldesley score his 100th century in first-class cricket in 1934?

190 Who scored a century at The Oval in 1934 to secure the Championship for Lancashire?

191 What was the result of the match at The Oval when Lancashire played the Rest of England in 1934?

192 Who carried his bat for 49 through an innings of 124 against Worcestershire at Old Trafford in 1935?

193 Which openers put on 208 against Kent in 1935?

194 Who hit 112 in an hour at Old Trafford in 1935 against Lancashire?

195 Who carried his bat through a Lancashire innings at Nelson against Somerset in 1931?

PICTURE QUIZ – 4

Who is doing what?

THE SECOND WORLD WAR AND AFTER

196 Who requisitioned Old Trafford during the Second World War?

197 Which Australian leader made a special visit to Old Trafford to see what damage had been done during the air raids?

198 Which Lancashire player scored 133 playing for the North of England v. R.A.A.F in 1944?

199 Who was paid three farthings an hour in 1945 to help tidy up the ground and buildings at Old Trafford ready for the cricket to begin again?

200 For whose benefit was the three day match against Yorkshire at Bradford in 1945 played?

201 Which Lancashire players took part in the Victory Test at Old Trafford in 1945?

202 Who captained Lancashire in 1946?

203 Which Lancashire cricketer was killed in a road accident just before the 1946 season?

204 In 1949, who took all ten wickets in an innings against Lancashire?

205 Which Lancashire player was chosen to lead the M.C.C. team to India and Pakistan in 1951-52?

CRICKET IN THE 1950s

206 In the match against Surrey at Old Trafford in 1953, how did Brian Statham (unintentionally) infringe the laws of cricket?

207 Who was the first player to be capped by three counties?

208 In whose Benefit match in 1953 did Roy Tattersall take 13 for 69?

209 Who played in four matches in 1950-51 and was born in Parramatta (New South Wales)?

210 Who was never awarded his first XI Cap but performed the hat-trick against Essex?

211 In 1957, Lancashire were defeated twice in two days at Aigburth. By whom?

212 Name two brothers who made their debut for Lancashire in 1951?

213 In 1959, who set a new wicket-keeping record for Lancashire of the most dismissals in a match?

214 Who took seven wickets for no runs off 19 balls in 1953?

215 Which Lancashire bowler took nine wickets for 116 in the 1950 Test against the West Indies at Old Trafford?

216 Who took 30 runs off John Ikin in one over in 1955?

217 He also scored a four and a six off the next two deliveries. Who was the bowler?

218 In 1956 Lancashire defeated Leicestershire without losing a wicket in either innings. Who were the two batsmen?

219 Who was the first Lancashire player to score a hundred in a Test at Old Trafford?

220 Who scored his only century for Lancashire in 1951 against Kent?

221 Who scored seven centuries for Lancashire in the same year?

222 In 1950, Lancashire shared the Championship with the team they played in the last match. Who was it?

223 What was Australia's score in the second innings at the end of the Test in 1953?

224 Whose highest score for Lancashire was against the Australians in 1957 when he scored 46, including seven fours in the only season he played first-class cricket?

225 Who was chosen as 'The Young Cricketer of the Year' in 1959?

CRICKET IN THE 1960s

226 Who topped the Lancashire bowling averages for 16 consecutive seasons?

227 Who played for Lancashire in 1963 and later played for Australia?

228 Who came from Northumberland and scored his first hundred against Yorkshire?

229 In 1961, Lancashire recorded a highest score against the Australians of 346. Who scored almost half the runs?

230 Who took five for one against Hampshire at Blackpool in 1967?

231 Who was the South African off-spinner who played one match for Lancashire in 1967?

232 Whose arm was broken during the 1963 season by West Indian Wes Hall?

233 In the first-ever Gillette Cup match who took five for 28?

234 In 1968 who became the first Lancashire player ever to perform a hat-trick against Yorkshire?

235 When was the first occasion that Lancashire reached the semi-final of the Gillette Cup?

236 In 1966, who obtained his highest score for Lancashire against the West Indies?

237 Whose last match for Lancashire was against Yorkshire in 1968?

238 Who played in 154 matches between 1963 and 1976, primarily as a batsman, but never scored a hundred?

239 Whose best bowling performance was eight for 121 against Yorkshire in 1964?

240 Who shared a double century partnership against Leicestershire in 1963 and later played for Leicestershire?

241 Which other Lancashire player went to Leicestershire and joined them in 1972?

242 Whose last century for Lancashire was at Southport in 1964?

243 Who joined Lancashire from Somerset in 1967 and scored over 1,000 runs in his first season?

244 In which year did Lancashire finish 15th in the Championship table and only lose one match?

245 In 1968, during the course of the opening match, who passed 20,000 runs in first-class cricket?

CRICKET IN THE 1970s

246 Who scored two centuries in the same match against Warwickshire in 1970?

247 Barry Wood shared in four double century partnerships, three for the first wicket and one for the third, all with the same partner. Who was his partner?

248 In 1979, the record partnership for the eighth wicket was broken by whom?

249 Who joined Lancashire in 1972 after being dismissed by another county,and took almost 500 wickets in 11 seasons?

250 A South African, he played one match for Lancashire in 1979 and took two for 58. Who was he?

251 In 1973, Farokh Engineer claimed eight victims in a match. On how many occasions did he achieve this feat?

252 In 1976 and 1977 Lancashire established an unenviable record. What was it?

253 Who started his career as a leg-break bowler, only took one wicket, but scored over 15,000 runs?

254 In Bombay in 1975, who scored 242 not out?

255 Who scored 94 on his debut against Middlesex in 1970?

PICTURE QUIZ – 5

This signalled a victory for whom in 1966?

256 He made his debut in 1973 but was not capped until 1982. Who is he?

257 Who moved from Lancashire to Leicestershire in 1977?

258 Who came from Somerset in 1975 and went to Hampshire in 1977?

259 In 1972 they recorded the second-highest partnership for any wicket since 1947. Who were they?

260 Who played in nine first-class matches for Lancashire, the first one in 1963 and the last one in 1971?

261 Who made his debut for Lancashire in 1967 and scored his first hundred in 1975?

262 Who were the two Lancashire players to be called up to play for England v. The Rest of the World XI in 1970?

263 Who scored 1,144 runs for Lancashire in his Benefit year?

264 Who was the Lancashire Captain in 1979?

265 Which Lancashire player completed 10,000 runs for Lancashire during the 1976 season?

1980s – I

266 How many consecutive wins did Lancashire have in the County Championship at the end of the 1987 season?

267 What was unique about Wasim Akram's achievement at Southport against Surrey in 1988?

268 Who was the Pakistani spin bowler who played for Lancashire in the early 1980s?

269 Who was recalled to the England side at the age of 39 for the one-day international against India in 1982?

270 Who was the Dane who played for Lancashire in 1985-86?

271 What was unique about Lancashire's victory over Leicestershire at Leicester in the County Championship in 1987?

272 Which two Lancashire players completed 10,000 runs in first-class cricket during the 1987 season?

273 Which players were awarded their County caps during the 1987 season?

274 Which two players put on 251 for the fourth wicket against Derbyshire at Derby in the last match of the 1988 season?

275 Who took five for eight against Leicestershire at Leicester in 1987 in only his third match for Lancashire?

1980s – 2

276 Which current Lancashire player has been capped by two other counties?

277 Which three current Lancashire players went to the same university?

278 Who scored over 1,000 runs for the Second XI in 1988?

279 Who scored a century before lunch against Lancashire in 1982?

280 Which team did Lancashire surprisingly lose to in 1983 in first-class cricket?

281 Who was the Lancashire player chosen to tour Australia in 1982-83?

282 Which Lancashire player fractured a leg while taking a run in a match at Lord's in 1982?

283 Which Lancashire player bowled 13 consecutive maiden overs against Gloucestershire in 1980?

284 Which four players who have played for Lancashire took part in the 1988 Minor Counties Championship final, playing for Cheshire?

285 On which ground did Warren Hegg score a maiden century in 1987?

CAPTAINS

286 Who died in New Orleans at the age of 33 and was an occasional Captain in 1899?

287 Who captained England after only one season in first-class cricket for Lancashire?

288 What distinction was shared by M.R. Barton (Surrey) and Nigel Howard?

289 Who were the two Lancashire players who played and captained the side in their only season in first-class cricket?

290 Which Lancashire Captain was killed in a flying accident?
291 He captained Lancashire to three succcessive Championships. Who was he?
292 Put this list of Captains in the order of when they were appointed Captain of the County: Bob Barber, Ken Grieves, Ken Cranston, Cyril Washbrook, Nigel Howard, Joe Blackledge.
293 Who was Lancashire's first regular Captain?
294 What other office did A.N. Hornby hold in 1894 as well as being Captain?
295 Who was Lancashire's first professional Captain?

LANCASHIRE PLAYERS

296 Name the players who have played 500 or more matches for Lancashire?
297 Who did Malcolm Hilton share a Benefit with in 1960?
298 Who are the two players who scored 1,000 runs for Lancashire in their first season in first-class cricket?
299 Who was the last Lancashire player to perform the 'double' of 1,000 runs and 100 wickets in a season?
300 Which Lancashire player captained the Gentlemen v. Players in 1952?
301 Who was Lancashire's first beneficiary?
302 Which player played both as a professional and as an amateur for the County before 1930?
303 Who started on the staff at Old Trafford as a medium-pace bowler but changed to off-spin and took over 150 wickets in the following season?
304 What was special about Johnny Briggs' 15 wickets against South Africa in 1888-89?
305 What was unusual and a great honour to Lancashire in the M.C.C. Tour of South Africa 1930-31?

PICTURE QUIZ – 6

Lancashire beat Yorkshire off the last ball. When?

PREVIOUS ADDRESSES

306 Who was born in Dukinfield and played for Lancashire and Northamptonshire?

307 Who scored his first century for Lancashire against Leicestershire at Blackpool and later on scored a century for Leicestershire against Lancashire?

308 Which Lancashire bowler died at the age of 94, preferring to play the major part of his county cricket in the Minor Counties competition?

309 Who was the Lancashire batsman who failed to achieve a Championship century but has scored many for Cheshire in the Minor Counties?

310 Which famous Australian batsman played one match for Lancashire, had one innings and was out for three?

311 He played one match for Lancashire, then captained Leicestershire from 1890 to 1906. Who was he?

312 He was a prominent member of the Transvaal club from 1976 to 1979 after playing one match for Lancashire in 1967. Can you name him?

313 Which Lancashire player has played for the most Counties?

314 Which Lancashire player, after he had left the County,took all ten wickets in an innings?

315 Who was born in New Orleans and played in 160 matches between1897 and 1909?

316 Which player scored two centuries in the same match against Lancashire and the following year joined Lancashire?

317 Who played for Yorkshire in one match until it was disclosed he had been born 20 yards outside the county boundary? He later went on to play over 150 matches for Lancashire?

318 Can you name six players who have played for both Lancashire and Leicestershire since the Second World War?

319 Name five players who have played for Lancashire and Somerset?

320 Who were the four South African born players to play for Lancashire since the Second World War?

MISSING NAMES

321 Archibald . . . MacLaren.
322 Joseph William Henry . . .
323 . . . Maneksha . . .
324 Richard . . . Barlow.
325 Paul John . . . Allott.
326 Sydney . . . Barnes.
327 Colin Everton Hunte . . .
328 Peter Thorp . . .
329 Eric Washington . . .
330 Albert . . . Hornby.
331 Peter . . . Lee.
332 Leslie Leopold . . .
333 Kenneth . . . McLeod.
334 Peter . . . Marner.
335 Dr Leslie Oswald Sheridan . . .
336 Bernard . . . Reidy.
337 Vernon Peter Fanshawe Archer . . .
338 Reginald . . . Spooner.
339 James . . . Tyldesley.
340 Leonard . . . Wilkinson.

JACK SIMMONS

341 Which County did Jack Simmons take his hat-trick against and on which ground?
342 What record did he break in 1980 for Lancashire?
343 Who was his 1,000th victim in first-class cricket?
344 What is his particular cricketing superstition?
345 On which ground did he take 12 for 123, the best match figures of his career in 1987?

ERNEST TYLDESLEY

346 In what year did Ernest Tyldesley score his first century for Lancashire?

347 Against whom did he score his 100th century and on which ground?
348 How old was he when he scored his 107 against Notts with Larwood and Voce at their fiercest?
349 How many runs did he score in 1928?
350 When did he retire from first-class cricket?

NICKNAMES

351 Shake.
352 Ranji.
353 Deep.
354 Sawdust.
355 George.
356 Jasper.
357 Tiddley.
358 Monkey.
359 Hubert.
360 Buddy.
361 Bud.
362 Plank.
363 Chimp.
364 Leapy.
365 Henry.
366 Bumble.
367 Budgie.
368 Lol.
369 Albert.
370 Thatch.

YOUNGEST/OLDEST

371 Which Lancashire player was the first 'Young Cricketer of the Year'?
372 Who was the last Lancashire player to score 1,000 runs in first-class cricket in his debut season?

373 Who is the youngest cricketer to appear for Lancashire?

374 Who is Lancashire's oldest cricketer to take the field for the County?

375 In how many seasons did A.N. Hornby appear for Lancashire?

376 Who is Lancashire's youngest Captain?

377 Which player was the youngest to score 1,000 runs for Lancashire and also score a century (different seasons)?

378 Who was the youngest player to score 2,000 runs in a season for Lancashire?

379 Who is the oldest player to score a century for Lancashire?

380 Who is the oldest player to captain Lancashire?

PICTURE QUIZ – 7

Barry Wood is injured but who were Lancashire playing?

RELATIVELY SPEAKING

381 How many runs did John and Ernest Tyldesley score together in first-class cricket for Lancashire? (a) over 40,000; (b) over 50,000; (c) over 60,000.

382 Which Lancashire player had a twin brother who dismissed him in a first-class match in the 1980s?

383 What record did J.T. and G.E. Tyldesley set in 1913 for Lancashire?

384 Geoff and Eric Edrich had two brothers who played first-class cricket. Who did they play for?

385 Who was Clive Lloyd's cousin who played for the West Indies?

386 Which family had four brothers in the same Lancashire team?

387 How many Hiltons have played for Lancashire?

388 How many Howards have played for Lancashire?

389 Were any related?

390 Which four sets of brothers have played for Lancashire since the Second World War?

CYRIL WASHBROOK

391 How many century partnerships did Len Hutton and Cyril Washbrook score in Test cricket?

392 Cyril Washbrook scored 1,000 runs in all first-class matches in the month of July 1946. Who was the other Lancastrian to achieve this in July?

393 What was remarkable about his first game for the Second XI for Lancashire?

394 How many centuries did he score in his first-class career?

395 On which ground was Cyril Washbrook recalled to the England side at the age of 42 to score 98?

A.C. MACLAREN

396 Why was A.C. MacLaren going to play for Hampshire and live in the south of England in 1902?

397 Which public school did he attend?

398 How did Lancashire recognise the batting feats of MacLaren in 1895?

399 Whom did he succeed as England Captain in 1899?

400 How many did he score in his last first-class match?

PICTURE QUIZ – 8

Lancashire had four wicket-keepers in 1956. Who are they?

JOHNNY BRIGGS

401 How old was he when he made his debut for Lancashire?
402 Which rugby club did Johnny Briggs play half-back for?
403 What unique record did he set during the Test matches against Australia in which he played?
404 In 1885 he was concerned in a batting feat which is still a Lancashire record. What was it?
405 Where did Johnny Briggs die?

BRIAN STATHAM

406 How many wickets did Brian Statham take for the County?
407 What was Brian Statham's highest score in first-class cricket?
408 Who was his Benefit match against in 1961?
409 How many Test wickets did he take for England?
410 Which match was Brian Statham's last for Lancashire?

CLIVE LLOYD

411 How many Tests did Clive Lloyd play for the West Indies?
412 Against which side did Clive Lloyd hit 217* for Lancashire at Old Trafford in 1971?
413 How many centuries has he scored in the Roses matches?
414 Against whom did Clive Lloyd hit 201* in only 120 minutes in 1969 for the West Indies?
415 What was Clive Lloyd's best season for Lancashire when he finished third in the national batting averages?

DAVID HUGHES

416 Where was David Hughes born?
417 In the semi-final of the Gillette Cup at Old Trafford in 1971, how many did he score in one over off J.B. Mortimore?

418 Whom did he hit for 26 off one over at Lords in the Gillette Cup final in 1976?

419 Which Australian side has David played for?

420 When was he awarded his County Cap?

EDDIE PAYNTER

421 Where did Eddie Paynter score 322 in one day?

422 What age was he when he scored his first County century for Lancashire?

423 What misfortune had Eddie Paynter suffered early in his life?

424 What role did Paynter play in the Test Match at Lords in 1938?

425 On which grounds did he score double centuries in Test Matches?

GEORGE DUCKWORTH

426 For which County did he have a trial before joining Lancashire?

427 In which year did he first play for England?

428 How many dismissals did he achieve in his career?

429 On which other sport did he commentate for the BBC?

430 In which year did he set a record for the most dismissals in a season for Lancashire?

WHO WAS HE?

431 Born in Ossett, Yorkshire, he played for both Yorkshire and Lancashire and went on to captain Derbyshire?

432 He played once for England and played Rugby League for Salford?

433 He scored 19,000 first-class runs and before joining Lancashire toured America and Brazil?

434 Who scored 1,228 and took 83 wickets in his first season in first-class cricket?

435 He scored a double century for England but his next highest Test score was under 50?

436 He topped 1,000 runs in a season for Lancashire 19 times?

437 He took 100 wickets in a season 11 times for Lancashire?

438 He performed the double of 1,000 runs and 100 wickets in a season twice for Lancashire?

439 Who paid for and designed his own headstone before he died, engraved 'Bowled at last'?

440 Who was the longest serving Lancashire scorer?

441 One of the best riders to hounds of his day, he played rugby for England on nine occasions; played for Blackburn Rovers at football, was a first-class runner and hurdler and boxed occasionally?

442 Who was presented with a stained-glass window with himself as a central figure?

443 He scored 38 first-class centuries with one double century and took 448 wickets and was born in Hereford?

444 Who are the two Lancashire batsmen to have each scored 152 in their second match for Lancashire?

445 He had a link with the County as a player and a coach that extended for 46 years?

446 Who took a hat-trick playing for the M.C.C. against Transvaal in 1956-57?

447 He played cricket for Yorkshire in 1946 and later served on the Lancashire committee?

448 Which Lancashire player participated in a record last-wicket partnership for England?

449 He kept wicket for Lancashire and later became Acker Bilk's agent?

450 He kept wicket for Lancashire and was a draughtsman in a biscuit factory?

451 He made his debut for Yorkshire in 1886 and then played for Lancashire, making 330 appearances?

452 He took more than 1,300 wickets in first-class cricket and four for 19 in the last Test Match of the Triangular Tournament in 1912?

PICTURE QUIZ – 9

A famed Lancashire player from 1899 to 1903 but who?

453 He took 150 wickets in 1920, 148 in 1921 and 142 in 1922 for Lancashire?

454 He was known as 't'owd chain-horse'?

455 He captained the Players at Lords, had a Test Match average of just under 60 and scored 20,000 runs in first-class cricket?

456 He went to school at Rugby, kept wicket and later became Treasurer of the Club?

457 He was a fast bowler who played soccer for Liverpool, Aston Villa and Leeds United?

458 He played for Cambridgeshire United and the All England XI and spent 48 years at Old Trafford?

459 He gained Blues at Cambridge for both soccer and cricket, appeared for Lancashire in 1878 and became Chairman and later President of the club?

460 He was top of the national bowling averages in 1950?

461 He was capped in 1975 for Lancashire and also in the same year he was chosen as the 'Young Cricketer of the Year' by the Cricket Writers' Club?

462 He took 100 wickets for the County seven times in eight seasons after the Second World War?

463 He scored 2,157 runs for Lancashire in 1959 and averaged over 40?

464 A future Lancashire Captain, he scored a century in only his second game for the County in 1933?

465 When he was 21, he took 145 wickets for Lancashire and was chosen to tour South Africa with the M.C.C.?

466 He took 131 wickets and scored 866 runs in 1937?

467 He played exactly 500 matches for Lancashire?

468 He was born in Tasmania and was killed in a road accident near Bolton. He played 11 Tests for Australia?

469 He came from Australia, played for Lancashire and kept goal for Bolton Wanderers and Bury?

470 Who scored a century for Lancashire at Liverpool against a County side captained by his brother?

BIRTHPLACES

Name the Lancashire players born in the following places:

471 Eaglescliffe, Co. Durham.
472 Barrow Bridge, Bolton.
473 Luansaya, N. Rhodesia.
474 Barrow, Clitheroe.
475 Portland, Jamaica.
476 North Shields, Northumberland.
477 Salt River, Cape Town, South Africa.
478 Aigburth, Liverpool.
479 Sutton-in-Ashfield, Notts. (two famous bowlers).
480 Lingwood, Norfolk.
481 Kidsgrove, Staffordshire.
482 Kumasi, Gold Coast.
483 Llanergan, Caernarvon.
484 Burwood, Sydney, Australia.
485 Thurscoe, Yorkshire.
486 Gosport, Hampshire.
487 Georgetown, British Guiana.
488 Middlesbrough, Yorkshire.
489 Columbo, Ceylon.
490 Litherland.

BENEFITS

491 Whose Benefit in the last century was affected because Lancashire lost by ten wickets on the second day?
492 Which bowler was unwell and so had to sit out his Benefit match?
493 Which two Yorkshiremen had Benefits for Lancashire in the same year?
494 Who scored a double century in Jack Sharp's Benefit match?
495 Who took 107 wickets in his Benefit year?
496 Who, by refusing to play on a wicket which had been covered, caused Johnny Briggs' Benefit match to be over in two days?

497 In 1884, Yorkshire and Lancashire players came together to form an 'England XI' for which Derbyshire player's Benefit?

498 Whose Benefit match against Yorkshire was ruined because of rain?

499 Who shared a Benefit in 1975?

500 Which four players had both a Benefit and a Testimonial for the County?

OPENERS

501 What is the lowest score by a batsman carrying his bat through an innings for Lancashire and who achieved this?

502 What was unusual about David Green's 2,037 runs scored during the 1965 season?

503 Who are the last two openers to score first wicket century stands in both innings?

504 Against which side did Gehan Mendis 'carry his bat' in 1988?

505 When, prior to the above, was the last time this feat was achieved for Lancashire and on which ground?

506 Who was the last Lancashire player to score 100 before lunch?

507 Which Lancashire player scored 171, 105 and 132* in successive innings in 1947?

508 Which opener has carried his bat through an innings most times for Lancashire?

509 Which two Lancashire openers put on 272 for the first wicket against Oxford University at Oxford in 1962?

510 Which pair of opening batsmen have shared in two partnerships of over 250 for the first wicket against Lancashire?

GREAT BATTING

511 Who is the only Lancashire player to score 1,000 runs in May?

512 In what year did he achieve this feat?

PICTURE QUIZ – 10

He played 19 matches for Lancashire in 1979 and 1980. Who is the bowler?

513 Who has scored 2,633 runs for Lancashire in a season?

514 Who was the first batsman to score 1,000 runs in a season for the County?

515 Who are the players who have scored over 20,000 runs for Lancashire?

516 What record did C. Washbrook and E. Tyldesley share in 1946 and 1926 respectively?

517 Who was the last batsman to score 2,000 runs in a season for Lancashire?

518 Who were the two batsmen to score over 250 for Lancashire since the Second World War?

519 Who were the two batsmen since the Second World War to score over 250 against Lancashire?

520 Who has scored the most double centuries for Lancashire?

CENTURIES

521 Who was the Lancashire player who scored the first Test century against the West Indians?

522 Which Lancashire player scored the 100th century in Test cricket in 1909?

523 Who were the two batsmen to score 100 centuries and make their 100th century against Lancashire?

524 Name two of the three Lancashire players who have scored a century on their first appearance for the county?

525 What was unusual about Graeme Fowler's two centuries in a match at Southport in 1982?

526 Who is the only Lancashire player to score four hundreds in successive innings?

527 When did he accomplish this?

528 Which Lancashire player scored exactly 100 on three occasions in the last eight seasons?

529 Steve O'Shaughnessy holds the record for the fastest century for Lancashire. Who held the record before?

530 Who was the last Lancashire player to score two hundreds in a match at Old Trafford?

CENTURIES

531 Name the two Lancashire players who have scored centuries against every first-class County?

532 Which two Lancashire players made their maiden centuries for Lancashire against Somerset in 1985?

533 Who scored nine centuries for Lancashire in 1947?

534 Which two Lancashire batsmen each scored 100 before lunch against Sussex in the same match?

535 Who was the Yorkshireman who scored the first century for the County?

536 A clergyman was the first amateur to score a century for Lancashire. Who was he?

537 Who scored a century on his first appearance in first-class cricket and another on his last 33 years later?

538 Who scored ten centuries for Lancashire against Warwickshire at Edgbaston?

539 Who scored a century before lunch three times for Lancashire?

540 Who scored 139* against Hampshire at Portsmouth in 1984, his only century for Lancashire, and scored 31 centuries while playing for another county?

DOUBLE CENTURIES AND MORE

541 Who scored 201* against Warwickshire at Nuneaton in 1984?

542 R. H. Moore of Hampshire scored 300 on 28 July 1937. Who was the Lancashire player to also score 300 on that day?

543 Who has scored four double centuries at Old Trafford since the Second World War?

544 Who was the only Lancashire player to score a double century for the County in the 1970s?

545 Where did he score this double century?

546 Who were the two Lancashire players to score double centuries for the County in 1984?

547 Who made three scores of over 200 in one season for Lancashire?

548 Who were the two batsmen (one from Lancashire) to score double centuries at Liverpool?

549 Which three Lancashire batsmen have scored triple centuries?

550 Who is the last Lancashire batsman to score a double century for Lancashire?

NOTABLE PARTNERSHIPS

551 Who added 423 runs for the seventh wicket in a second XI match against Derbyshire in 1984?

552 Lancashire's last wicket partnership of 173 has stood for over 100 years. Who were the two batsmen?

553 What record do Graeme Fowler and Steve O'Shaughnessy hold together?

554 On which ground did A.C. MacLaren and R.H. Spooner make their record first wicket stand of 368 in 1903?

555 Who was it against?

556 Which Lancashire wicket-keeper holds the record along with R.M. Ratcliffe for the eighth wicket partnership of 158?

557 Who were the two Surrey batsmen who made the record partnership of 172 for the tenth wicket against Lancashire in 1982?

558 Who shared with Barry Wood in a record 1975 partnership of 249 at Edgbaston against Warwickshire?

559 Which wicket was the partnership for?

560 Who were the two Australians who hold the record for the eighth wicket for Lancashire?

PICTURE QUIZ – II

A Lancashire player in a different guise.

FIELDING AND WICKET-KEEPING

561 Which Lancashire wicket-keeper was described as 'The Prince of Wicket-keepers'?

562 Who took a catch off Tich Freeman at Old Trafford in 1928 in a Test Match when he came on as substitute but was never capped by Lancashire?

563 Which Lancashire player kept wicket for England in a one-day international?

564 Who is the only Lancashire fielder to take over 50 catches for the County in a season?

565 What years did he accomplish this?

566 Which Lancashire fielder of the 19th century was regarded as 'one of the greatest ever cover-point fielders'?

567 Which two Lancashire players share the record for the most catches in an innings?

568 Which three wicket-keepers have taken the most catches/ stumpings for Lancashire?

569 Which wicket-keeper holds the record for the most dismissals in an innings for Lancashire?

570 Which two wicket-keepers hold the record for the most dismissals in a match?

GREAT BOWLING

571 Who took 13 wickets at Aigburth against Warwickshire and 14 wickets against Somerset at Old Trafford in 1909?

572 Who took nine for 47 before lunch for Lancashire against Somerset at Old Trafford and the eight for 90 in the second innings in 1905?

573 Who took all ten wickets at Old Trafford against Worcestershire in 1900?

574 Which two bowlers shared all 20 Surrey wickets at Old Trafford in 1903?

575 He took a Test hat-trick in one game and three wickets in four balls in another Test. Who was he?

576 Who was the last player to take all ten wickets in an innings for Lancashire?
577 Which player has taken the most wickets for Lancashire?
578 Whose first wicket in County cricket was that of George Headley?
579 Who clean bowled W.G. Grace on 13 occasions?
580 Who bowled the most balls (630) in a County Championship game?

GREAT BOWLING

581 Who lost by two hours to Wilfred Rhodes the race to be first to take 100 wickets in a season on 5 July 1911?
582 Who are the two Lancashire bowlers to take over 2,000 first-class wickets?
583 Who took 2,000 wickets in the fewest number of matches?
584 Who had a spell of bowling in which he took seven wickets in 19 balls including four wickets in five balls?
585 Who are the two Lancashire bowlers who have each taken 17 wickets in a match for Lancashire?
586 Who took the most wickets in a season for Lancashire?
587 How many wickets did he take?
588 Who are the only two Lancashire bowlers to take three hat-tricks for the County?
589 Which Lancashire bowler in 1889 took 102 wickets in first-class cricket in his first season for Lancashire at the age of 24?
590 Who is the only Lancashire player to take ten wickets and score a century in the same match three times?

GREAT BOWLING

591 Which Lancashire player is the only one to take a hat-trick and score a 50 in the same match?
592 Who was the last player to take eight wickets in an innings for Lancashire?

593 What great bowling feat did V.E. Walker perform in the first County match at Old Trafford in 1865 playing for Middlesex?
594 Which three Lancashire bowlers took 100 or more wickets each in 1959 and 1960 for Lancashire?
595 Who took 183 wickets in all first-class matches in 1911, more than anyone else in the country?
596 Who are the only two Lancashire bowlers to take 200 wickets in a season twice?
597 Which Lancashire player bowled five Surrey batsmen for one run at The Oval in 1882 but later left the game because of a failure to meet residential qualifications?
598 Who was the first Lancashire player to complete the 'double' of 1,000 runs and 100 wickets in a season?
599 Where was he born?
600 Which Lancashire player did the double of 1,000 runs and 100 wickets in 1904?

THE TORTOISE AND THE HARE

601 Who hit a century before lunch at Bath in 1906 against Somerset and went on to score 240?
602 Who batted for 74 minutes before scoring in a Roses match at Sheffield in 1969?
603 How many runs did Frank Hayes hit in one over off M. Nash against Glamorgan at Swansea in 1977?
604 How many minutes did Steve O'Shaughnessy take for his record century in 1983?
605 Which Leicestershire bowler conceded over 100 runs?
606 How many scoring strokes did O'Shaughnessy take for his century?
607 Who hit a century in only 43 minutes for Lancashire in 1905?
608 Lancashire scored at a rate of 131 runs per 100 balls against whom?
609 Against Notts in 1875 he scored 44 out of the first 45 runs scored. Who was he?

PICTURE QUIZ – 12

Who is this former Lancashire player?

610 Who scored a century before lunch for both Worcestershire and Lancashire?

DEBUTS

611 Who made his debut for the County in 1908, scoring 131*, and was also no-balled for throwing in the match?

612 In 1906 at Old Trafford which player, making his debut for Kent, made a duck and took one for 103?

613 He scored a century on his debut for Lancashire and on his debut in Australia and America. Who was he?

614 Who made his debut for Lancashire on his 20th birthday, 17 June 1950?

615 Who scored 1,066 in his first season for Lancashire, aged 24?

616 Who was the last Lancashire player to score 1,000 runs in his first year in first-class cricket?

617 Who made 99 on his debut for Lancashire in 1901 against Essex at Leyton but only played six matches for the County?

618 How many runs did Frank Hayes score on his debut for Lancashire?

619 Who was the Lancashire player to make his debut in a Test Match at the age of 38?

620 Who took four for 81 on his debut and only match for Lancashire?

LANCASHIRE PLAYERS IN TEST CRICKET

621 He once took 15 wickets in a Test Match in South Africa. Who was he?

622 In 1966, England lost 3-1 to the West Indies. Who was the only Lancashire player to play in all five Tests?

623 When was Cyril Washbrook recalled after being given out in a Test?

624 Which Lancashire player has won the most England caps?
625 Who went in as nightwatchman in a Test at Headingley in 1930 and batted on three separate days for 33?
626 Which Lancashire player has kept wicket in a Test Match for England since the Second World War?
627 Name the five Lancashire players who have captained England in a Test Match.
628 Which two Lancashire players were capped and also chosen to tour Australia in 1970-71?
629 Who made his Test debut against the West Indies in 1939 in the Lord's Test, scored a total of 99 runs but never played for England again?
630 Who was the only batsman in the bodyline series to have a higher batting average than Don Bradman?

PICTURE QUIZ – 13

Can you name the Lancashire players and the year?

LANCASHIRE PLAYERS IN TEST CRICKET

631 Which Lancashire left-arm bowler bowled unchanged in a Test innings at Sydney to take seven for 40?

632 Who clean bowled most batsmen in a single innings in a Test Match?

633 Which Lancashire opening batsman got a wicket in his first over in Test cricket?

634 Which Lancashire player holds the record for the most wickets in a Test series?

635 Who took the last four South African wickets in an over at Headingley in 1947?

636 Who is the only Lancashire player to take a hat-trick against Australia?

637 Which Lancashire player was chosen for England in 1909 and was the only English player to score a century in the series?

638 Which Lancashire player took six South African wickets in his first Test Match?

639 What unique feat did two Lancashire cricketers achieve on the tour to South Africa in 1930-31?

640 In 1953, Lancashire fielded a side with nine Test players in it. Who were they?

TEST DEBUTS

641 Which Lancashire player took seven for 74 on his Test debut?

642 Which Lancashire player played in the 'Victory' Test in 1945 but did not play in an official Test match?

643 Who played for England during his first season for Lancashire?

644 Who was the oldest Lancashire player to make his Test debut?

645 A Lancashire player made his Test debut in the series against South Africa in 1947. Who was he?

PICTURE QUIZ – 14

Who is the bowler, and what match is it?

646 Who took five wickets in an innings on his Test debut for England in 1946?

647 Where did Graeme Fowler make his Test debut for England and who was it against?

648 Who are the four Lancashire players who made their Test debuts at Old Trafford since the Second World War?

649 Which Lancashire player took a wicket with his first ball in Test cricket?

650 Which two Lancashire cricketers made their Test debuts within 12 months of their first-class debuts?

LAKER'S TEST MATCH 1956

651 Who took the other wicket for England?

652 From which end of the ground did he take each of the 19 wickets?

653 Who was the only Australian not to be dismissed twice by Laker in the match?

654 Which English batsmen made centuries in the match?

655 Which English fielder took five catches in the match?

656 Where was Jim Laker born?

657 Which two Australians 'bagged a pair' in the match?

658 Who top scored for Australia in both innings?

659 Which Lancashire players played in this match?

660 What other bowling feat did Laker perform for Surrey that year?

TEST CRICKET AT OLD TRAFFORD

661 The first time a player scored a century before lunch in a Test Match happened at Old Trafford. Who was the player and what was the year?

662 What was unusual about the England totals in the 1976 match against the West Indians?

663 Who batted on four separate days in an innings of 38?

664 Who batted in 1984 against the West Indies with a broken arm?

665 Who was the 'Man of the Match' in the 1980 Test at Old Trafford?

666 Which Test Match at Old Trafford is famous because of the failure of one player?

667 What was special about Brian Close's Test debut against New Zealand in 1949?

668 Which two West Indian batsmen scored centuries in the 1966 Test Match?

669 Who took ten wickets in this match?

670 How many wickets did Malcolm Marshall take in the England second innings in 1988?

TEST CRICKET AT OLD TRAFFORD

671 Who captained England for the first time at Old Trafford in 1969 with a win against the West Indies?

672 Which Lancashire player made his highest score in first-class cricket in the 1971 Old Trafford Test Match against India?

673 Which two wicket-keepers bowled in Test Matches at Old Trafford?

674 Who scored centuries in both innings of the 1976 Old Trafford Test?

675 Who scored 112 for India on his Test debut as an Oxford undergraduate at Old Trafford in 1959, aged 20?

676 When R.B. Simpson scored 311* for Australia in 1964, who also scored a century for Australia?

677 Who bowled 95.1 overs for Australia in the England innings?

678 What record did Ken Barrington set with his 256 in the match?

679 Who beat England in 1955 at Old Trafford to record England's first defeat on this ground since 1902?

680 Who deputised as wicket-keeper for Evans who was injured during the match?

TEST CRICKET AT OLD TRAFFORD

681 Who dismissed John Dyson, Kim Hughes and Graham Yallop in one over at Old Trafford in 1981?

682 Who bowled a 13-ball over at Old Trafford?

683 Who bowled 77 overs on his Test debut which was at Old Trafford in 1964?

684 Which Australian player bowled two successive overs in a Test Match at Old Trafford?

685 Who took one wicket in a Test at Old Trafford and why is it remembered?

686 Which bowler did the hat-trick in each innings of a Test Match at Old Trafford?

687 In which years were England dismissed for under 100 by the West Indies?

688 Who was named 'Man of the Match' in the first Test Match of 1987 at Old Trafford against Pakistan?

689 Which team at Old Trafford became the first side to be dismissed twice in a day in a Test Match?

690 Who scored 182 for the West Indies in the Test Match of 1963?

ONE-DAY INTERNATIONALS AT OLD TRAFFORD

691 The lowest innings score in a one-day international is 45. By which team at Old Trafford?

692 Who scored 142 not out against New Zealand at Old Trafford in 1986?

693 The West Indies were defeated for the first time in Prudential Cup Matches in 1983. By whom?

694 When was the first one-day international played at Old Trafford and who was it against?

PICTURE QUIZ – 15

Peter Lever is bowling but who were Lancashire playing?

695 Who scored a century in this match?

696 Which New Zealand batsman scored a century in the Prudential Cup Match in 1975?

697 Who was bowled out for 85 in 1978, their lowest one-day score?

698 Who did Viv Richards share a century partnership with for the tenth wicket in 1984?

699 Which milestone did he pass during his 189?

700 Who scored 75 for England in this match?

CRICKET AND FOOTBALL

701 Which F.A. Cup final team in 1906 had two players who also played cricket for Lancashire?

702 Name the two players, who also played Test cricket for England?

703 Which Lancashire player scored a goal in the 1956 Cup final?

704 Who is the last Lancashire player to play League football?

705 Which Lancashire bowler played for Port Vale?

706 Which Lancashire all-rounder played football for Chester?

707 Who appeared for Manchester United in the 1958 Cup final and also played cricket for Lancashire?

708 Which Lancashire player was a referee in the F.A. Cup tie when Preston beat Hyde 26-0?

709 Which Lancashire cricketer played for Tranmere, West Bromwich Albion and Aston Villa?

710 Which Lancashire cricketer captained Derby County, Sheffield Wednesday, Burnley and also played for Bolton Wanderers?

CRICKET AND OTHER SPORTS

711 Which Lancashire cricketer played Rugby League for Salford?

712 In which other sport did R.H. Spooner represent England?

PICTURE QUIZ – 16

Who is the batsman?

713 Who left Lancashire to become Secretary of Salford Rugby League Club?

714 Which Rugby League clubs was Jack Wood Secretary of before becoming Secretary of Lancashire?

715 Which Lancashire opening batsman also threw the javelin for Cambridge University?

716 He was goalkeeper for Lancashire for 12 years and was also a very good sprint runner?

717 Who was the first person to appear for England in both a Test Match and a Rugby Union international?

718 Which Lancashire captain played hockey and Rugby Union for Lancashire?

719 Which Lancashire cricketer toured Australia with the British Isles Rugby Union side in 1888?

720 He played one match for Lancashire, 118 for Northants and football for Northampton Town, Charlton and Wolves. Who was he?

OTHERWISE OCCUPIED – I

721 Which Lancashire player became Assistant Secretary of Surrey C.C.C. and later Secretary of the M.C.C.?

722 Which Lancashire Test cricketer became Recorder of Oldham?

723 Which Lancashire player and Test cricketer was also an accomplished pianist?

724 Which two players went on to become Secretaries of the Club?

725 Who were the three clergymen to play for Lancashire?

726 Who was the manager of the 1946-47 M.C.C. side which toured Australia?

727 Which Lancashire player became 'Lord Rochdale'?

728 Which Lancashire player is also an accomplished drummer?

729 Who was the Australian doctor who played for Lancashire?

730 Which Lancashire player worked as a salesman for an undertakers during the winter months?

PICTURE QUIZ – 17

Who is conducting whom?

PICTURE QUIZ – 18

After he finished keeping wicket he became a publican in Middleton.

OTHERWISE OCCUPIED – 2

731 Which Lancashire player is a dentist?
732 How many Lancashire cricketers have become M.P.s?
733 Can you name any of them?
734 Who, when he left Lancashire, went on to become Secretary of Melbourne C.C., Australia?
735 Who was the former Lancashire player who was umpire when Gary Sobers hit six sixes in an over?
736 Which Lancashire player was a Director of Everton F.C.?
737 Which Lancashire cricketer was landlord at The Grosvenor in Blackpool and the Lord Nelson in Blackburn?
738 Which Lancashire player, born in Heywood in 1923, was elected Chairman of Pendle Magistrates
739 Which Lancashire batsman was appointed head groundsman and cricket coach at Cheltenham College?
740 Who resigned the captaincy of Lancashire when he was elected an M.P.?

BOOK TITLES

Name the authors of the following books concerning Lancashire cricket and cricketers:

741 Cuts and Glances
742 Archie
743 40 Seasons of First-Class Cricket
744 Cricket All The Way
745 55 Years Cricket Memories
746 50 Years Cricket Reminiscences of a Non-Player
747 Lancashire Hot-pot
748 Cricket Merry-go-Round
749 Cricket Old and New
750 The Roses Matches 1919-1939
751 Roses for Rememberance
752 Living for Cricket
753 Flat Jack

754 Cricket Triumphs and Troubles
755 Old Trafford
756 Cricket: The Wars of the Roses
757 Cricket: The Silver Lining
758 A Spell at the Top
759 Cricket Annual 1949
760 Lancashire Cricket at the Top

QUOTES AND AUTHORS

761 Who described whom as 'the Mercutio of cricket'?
762 In *Soldiers of the Willow*, a cricket song, Joe Darling (Australia) and which Lancashire player are celebrated?
763 Who said: 'First he runs you out, then he gives you a sovereign'?
764 Which Lancashire player did R.C. Robertson-Glasgow describe once as 'playing an innings of 83 which varied from almost tottering survival to an heroic assumption of dominance'?
765 What do Neville Cardus, L.E.G. Ames and Alan Miller have in common?

NEVILLE CARDUS AND LANCASHIRE

Can you name the Lancashire players who Neville Cardus described in the following quotes?

766 'He played cricket as some proud Roman might have played it.'
767 'He was fit to play in front of the Queen . . . and in her own drawing room too!'
768 'I wonder what became of him, for he was merely in his early twenties when he won an England Cap.'
769 'He shouldered his bat like a rifle and marched back to the refuge of his crease singing *The British Grenadier*.'

770 'A loveable great son of Old Trafford.'

771 'We have seen him in recent years at Test Matches, a spectator with Wilfred Rhodes, leading his equally famous and honoured old colleague to his seat.'

772 'I like the way he wears his cap; no cricket cap can seem as confident of peak as . . . can.'

773 'For . . . was very much a great wind blowing through cricket: the imagination sees him beating up over the wide expanse of Old Trafford, raising a merry dust.'

774 'Stubborn and canny, with no romantic nonsense about him, a shrewd fellow, biding his time.'

775 'He was surely born for a game, for he was a sort of little India-rubber ball of a man.'

TRUE OR FALSE? – I

Are these statements true or false?

776 P.G.H. Fender had a trial for Lancashire.

777 Len Hutton scored his 100th hundred against South Africa at Old Trafford in 1951.

778 In 1953, Alec Bedser took his 100th wicket of the season in the Test at Old Trafford.

779 George Tribe was a bowling coach at Old Trafford.

780 Johnny Briggs played for Lancashire in 1939.

781 Dick Tyldesley was Ernest's brother.

782 Jack Hallows and Charlie Hallows were father and son.

783 Barry Wood was the first Yorkshireman to score 100 for Lancashire in a Roses match.

784 George Best played cricket at Old Trafford.

785 Sheep dog trials were held at Old Trafford in 1947.

PICTURE QUIZ – 19

This was taken during his highest Test score. Who is he and who is the bowler?

TRUE OR FALSE? – 2

Are these statements true or false?

786 Blackpool has staged a Test Match.
787 A Lancashire player has played Test cricket for South Africa.
788 A.N. Hornby never usually wore a cap on the field.
789 E. Tyldesley scored 1,000 runs in Test cricket.
790 Geoff Pullar scored his first Test hundred at Old Trafford.
791 England played Australia at Old Trafford in 1988.
792 The Wilson stand at Old Trafford is named after wicket-keeper Alan Wilson.
793 The Pavilion was used as a hospital during the Second World War.
794 Dora Bryan's husband played for Lancashire.
795 Charlie Barnett scored 100 before lunch in a Test at Old Trafford.

ANAGRAMS

796 A Claw Stone.
797 'Reat' Tall Story.
798 Meagre Flower.
799 A Fresh Yank.
800 Lively Cold.
801 Crack Pine.
802 Rowdy Boar.
803 Shaming Need.
804 Driven Aged.
805 Not a No Ball.
806 Good Kiwi Then.
807 Harry W. Broad.
808 Lone Gardener.
809 Trouble New Liars.
810 Ignored Doris.
811 A Swank Front.

812 Red Brain Dyer.
813 Crank Sonnet.
814 Peel Tree.
815 Still Robber.

PICTURE QUIZ – 20

Who is the bowler and can you identify the wicket-keeper?

ONE-DAY MATCHES

816 Which batsmen have scored centuries in all three one-day competitions?
817 What one-day record did Lancashire achieve in 1970?
818 Which one-day competition did Lancashire win in 1981?

819 Who scored 149 for Lancashire in the Asda Trophy at Scarborough against Yorkshire in 1987?

820 How many one-day competitions did Lancashire win under the captaincy of Jack Bond?

821 Who was nominated as best bowler of the Asda competition in 1987?

822 Which non-first-class side have Lancashire lost to in the Benson & Hedges Cup Competition?

823 What was 'different' about the Refuge Cup in 1988?

824 What one-day competition did Lancashire take part in at Scarborough in 1988?

825 Which two Lancashire players were awarded 'Man of the Match' awards in the Refuge Cup in 1988?

NATWEST/GILLETTE CUP

826 Which Lancashire batsman scored the first century in this competition?

827 Who took seven for 32 against Lancashire in 1983, the first bowler to take seven wickets in the 60-over competition?

828 Which two Lancashire batsmen put on 234 for the fourth wicket in a 60-over match?

829 Which County side have Lancashire played most in this competition?

830 The most economical bowling in the competition was by a Lancashire player 12 – 9 – 3 – 1 against Suffolk in 1983. Who was it?

831 Who has scored the highest innings for Lancashire in this competition?

832 Who bowled Lancashire out for 59 in 1963?

833 What other Lancashire ground as well as Old Trafford have they played on in this competition?

834 Who has taken the most wickets for Lancashire in this competition?

835 Who are the three Lancashire batsmen to score over 1,000 runs?

836 How many 'Man of the Match' awards has Clive Lloyd won?

PICTURE QUIZ – 21

Played in one Test Match – ecclesiastical connections!

837 Who has taken a hat-trick for Lancashire in this competition?
838 How many times have Lancashire been losing semi-finalists?
839 Who scored two centuries for Lancashire during 1984 in two matches?
840 How many overs were played in the first year of the competition?

LANCASHIRE v. GLOUCESTERSHIRE SEMI-FINAL 1971

841 Who scored 65 for Gloucestershire in the match?
842 Who hit the winning run for Lancashire?
843 Can you fill in the scoring strokes from John Mortimore's over to David Hughes: —, —, two, —, —, —?
844 Who scored exactly 50 runs for Lancashire?
845 What time did the match finish?

SEVEN GILLETTE/NAT WEST CUP FINALS AT LORD'S

846 Who was the 'Man of the Match' in the 1970 Cup final?
847 Which Lancashire fielder won the 'Learie Constantine' award for the best fielder in the final of 1976?
848 Which other County has also won the Cup four times?
849 Which catch turned the 1971 Cup final against Kent for Lancashire?
850 Who did Lancashire play in the 1972 final when Clive Lloyd scored 126?
851 Have Lancashire ever won the NatWest Trophy and if so in which year?
852 Who scored 51 for Lancashire in the 1975 final against Middlesex?
853 Who did Lancashire lose to in the 1976 Cup final?
854 Who was the only Lancashire batsman to score a half-century in the 1986 final?
855 Who was the 'Man of the Match' in this final?

PICTURE QUIZ – 22

Played in 134 matches for Lancashire between the wars.

JOHN PLAYER/REFUGE ASSURANCE SUNDAY LEAGUE

856 Who were the first two Lancashire players to score centuries in the same match?

857 In which two years did Lancashire win the John Player League?

858 Who has scored most runs for Lancashire in a season in the Sunday League?

859 Who scored 100* in only 50 minutes in a John Player League match in 1974?

860 Who took a wicket on his debut in this country with his first ball?

861 In 1970, three Lancashire bowlers were in the top four of the John Player League bowling averages. Who were they?

862 Name the players who have played in the Sunday League for Lancashire but have not played in first-class cricket.

863 Who was Lancashire's youngest player to score a century in the Sunday League?

864 Who was the first player to score 1,000 runs in the Sunday League?

865 On which grounds have Lancashire played Sunday League cricket in the County?

866 Who took two wickets in the last over of the 1970 season and one with his first ball of the next season?

867 Which Lancashire wicket-keeper's son played for Derbyshire in the Sunday League in 1988?

868 Which three bowlers have each taken 26 wickets in a season in the Sunday League?

869 Who was the first cricketer to play for four Counties in the John Player League, and which were the Counties?

870 Which County holds the record for both the lowest score against Lancashire and Lancashire's lowest score?

871 Who are the Lancashire batsmen to score more than 4,000 runs in the Competition?

872 Who has made the most appearances for Lancashire in the Sunday League?

873 Who has captained the team most times in this Competition?

PICTURE QUIZ – 23

He was killed in a car accident in Staffordshire.

874 Which wicket-keeper has taken the most dismissals in this Competition for Lancashire?

875 Who has taken the most catches as a fielder in this Competition?

BENSON & HEDGES CUP

876 Which Lancashire players scored centuries in the same match in 1980?

877 Who was the adjudicator who gave John Abrahams the Gold Award for his captaincy in the 1984 final?

878 Which former Lancashire player performed the hat-trick in the 1974 Cup final?

879 Who has won the most Gold Awards for Lancashire?

880 Who dismissed Lancashire for 82, their lowest score in the Competition in 1972?

881 Who were the two Lancashire batsmen who shared a stand of 227 (third wicket) against Minor Counties North at Old Trafford in 1973?

882 Which Lancashire bowler recorded the best bowling performance for the County against Scotland at Old Trafford in 1982?

883 In the 1984 semi-final against Notts a young Lancashire batsman scored 87. Who was he?

884 Who were dismissed for 68 (the lowest total against Lancashire) in 1973 at Old Trafford?

885 Which team did Lancashire tie with in 1986 but won on a faster scoring rate?

ODDS AND ENDS

886 What rank in the Army did Leonard Green hold when he became President of the Club?

887 On which ground did Lancashire and Yorkshire play a 'Battle of the Roses' match in 1972?

PICTURE QUIZ – 24

Lancashire player who also captained Staffordshire.

888 Which two Lancashire batsmen players were five feet two-and-a-half inches and five feet two inches tall?

889 Which opening pair of Lancashire bowlers had 16 children between them?

890 Which Lancashire player helped organise 'Test' matches in a Japanese prisoner-of-war camp?

891 Which Lancashire bowler played football for Tranmere Rovers, West Bromwich Albion and Aston Villa?

892 His brother-in-law was a Lancashire batsman in the 1950s and 1960s. Who was he?

893 Which Lancashire player has the initials C.E.H.C.?

894 Which Lancashire player was named after an Australian cricketer?

895 Who was Lancashire's official statistician from 1954 to 1986?

896 When did Lancashire play against Lancashire?

897 Where in Manchester did Lancashire C.C. have their office prior to the Second World War?

898 In December 1974 four players who played for Lancashire played Test cricket for four different countries, can you name them?

899 Why didn't R.H. Spooner play first-class cricket in 1913?

900 Name the Lancashire players who have been Test selectors since the Second World War.

901 In what year did Lancashire celebrate their Diamond Jubilee?

902 Which Indian religious order did Farokh Engineer belong to?

903 Which two Lancashire professionals went on to become Presidents of the Club?

904 Which former Lancashire player stood as umpire in the 1961 Test at Old Trafford?

905 Who completed the first part of the double of 1,000 runs and 100 wickets in a season at Blackpool in 1984?

906 On which ground did MacLaren and Spooner put on 368 for the first wicket against Gloucestershire in 1903?

907 Who is the only Lancashire player to score centuries for Lancashire on five different Lancashire grounds?

908 Can you name the six Yorkshiremen who played for Lancashire in 1897?

PICTURE QUIZ – 25

A great bowler and a great batsman.

909 Which Lancashire player retired in 1961?
910 In May 1964 Lancashire were bowled out for 57. Who were the opponents?
911 Who made two not-out centuries against Warwickshire in the one match in 1970?
912 Who captained Lancashire in ten matches in 1956 when Cyril Washbrook was playing for England?
913 Which player was top scorer in the first County match at Preston against Gloucestershire in 1936?
914 Has L.S. Lowry ever painted a cricket match?
915 What award did David Hughes win in 1987?

CURIOUS

916 Who was called up to play for England in a one-day Prudential Trophy match when he had already batted twice in a County game?
917 Which Lancashire player won two Gillette Cup winners' medals in the same year?
918 Who is remembered in the Old Trafford museum by a red serviette?
919 Which cricket statistician played for Lancashire in a one-day 12-a-side match at Fazakerley in 1941?
920 Who piloted an aeroplane to take the Lancashire team to a County match in 1935?
921 Which Lancashire coach wrote an autobiography entitled *Never Cross a Bat*?
922 Which slow left-arm bowler took six for 73 against the Australians in 1948?
923 Which Lancashire Secretary refereed a semi-final of the F.A. Cup?
924 Six Tyldesleys played for Lancashire. Which four were brothers?
925 Who only scored two centuries in his career, one for a University and one against a University?

PICTURE QUIZ – 26

He scored 35 centuries for Lancashire.

TWENTY QUESTIONS

926 Who became Head Gardener on the Duke of Westminster's estate at Eaton Park?

927 Between 1933 and 1935 he took 279 wickets after returning to the County side from League cricket. Who?

928 Of whom did A.C. MacLaren say: 'He thumped me on the left thigh, he hit my gloves from a length. He actually said "Sorry sir" and I said "don't be sorry you're coming to Australia with me".'?

929 In the 1930s he played for Lancashire, Buckinghamshire, Nelson, Colne, Burnley and Lowerhouse. Who was he?

930 Who are the oldest Lancashire match sponsors?

931 Two Lancashire Treasurers had sons who became Captains of Lancashire. Who were they?

932 In 1938 two Lancashire bowlers took 285 wickets between them. Who were they?

933 Who opened the Indoor Sports Centre in 1969?

934 Which two Prime Ministers have attended matches at Old Trafford since the war?

935 Who is the only President since 1916 to have been in office for more than two years?

936 Only two members of the clergy have ever been President of the club. Who were they?

937 Since the Second World War how many Lancashire players have become first-class umpires?

938 How many of these have umpired in a Test Match?

939 How many groundsmen have Lancashire had since the Second World War?

940 Which Lancashire Secretary was also Secretary of Somerset and Hampshire?

941 In the match against Sussex in 1947, Lancashire declared when two batsmen were 19 runs short of breaking a record first wicket partnership which had stood since 1903. Who were the batsmen and what was the record?

942 In 1979 John Lyon and Bob Ratcliffe established a new record partnership for the eighth wicket. What was the previous record?

943 Which scorer was granted a Testimonial by the club?

944 Which County has Lancashire played most times next to Yorkshire in first-class cricket?

945 When did 120,417 people attend a Test Match at Old Trafford?

WHOSE AUTOGRAPH?

946

947

948

949

950

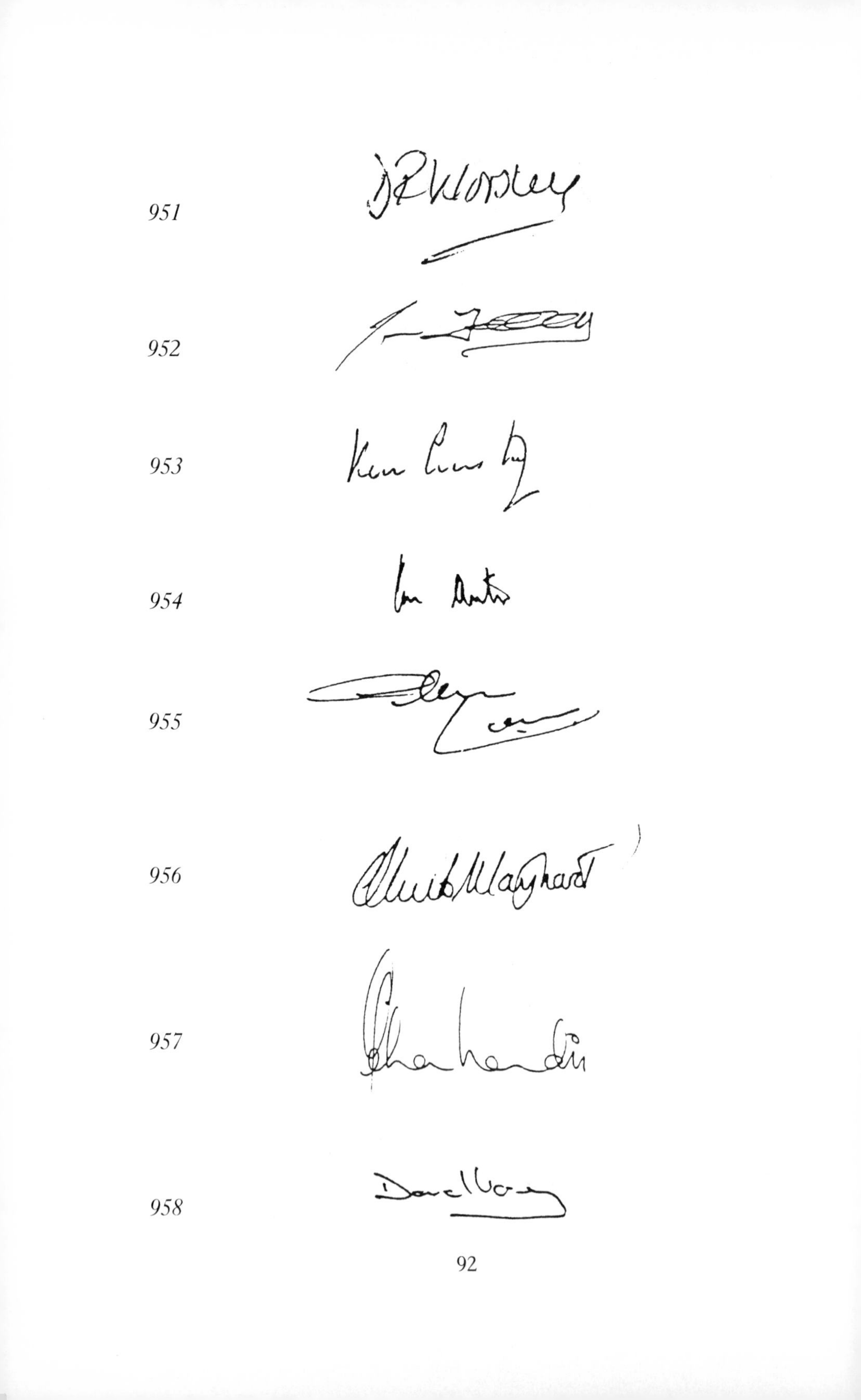

951

952

953

954

955

956

957

958

959

960

961

962

963

964

965

WORD SEARCH

Can you find seven Lancashire players?

A	S	H	N	O	C	P	L	W	T
L	E	M	I	N	O	R	Y	A	L
S	T	E	C	L	R	E	O	N	Y
E	R	N	A	L	T	W	D	F	A
T	A	D	N	O	E	O	L	I	T
R	L	I	S	Y	C	E	N	T	R
E	D	S	I	D	W	L	B	T	I
I	E	K	M	R	C	O	N	O	S
D	R	I	M	I	N	T	O	L	W
L	S	N	L	D	T	E	R	D	E

PICTURE QUIZ – 27

He took 707 wickets for Lancashire.

LAST SEASON

966 Which two players did Lancashire sign at the end of the 1988 season?

967 How many wickets did Dexter Fitton take in the Yorkshire second innings of the Roses Match at Old Trafford?

968 Who scored centuries in three competitions for Lancashire in 1988?

969 Which former Lancashire capped player died in 1988 who also played for Northants?

970 How many caps were awarded by Lancashire in 1988?

971 Which Lancashire player was chosen to play for the MCC against the Champion County in 1988?

972 Who was the only player to score a double-century against Lancashire in 1988?

973 Can you name the four players who made their first-class debuts for Lancashire during the 1988 season?

974 Who scored a century for Lancashire in the pre-season tour of Jamaica?

975 Which four Lancashire players were awarded the Carphone player of the month award during the season?

976 Which Bolton League club did Chris Matthews play for while he was with Lancashire?

977 Who took five wickets or more in an innings five times for Lancashire in 1988?

978 Who topped the Lancashire batting averages in first-class cricket in 1988?

979 Which school did both Michael Atherton and Mark Crawley attend?

980 What was discovered underneath the covers at the Parks during the match with Oxford University?

PICTURE QUIZ – 28

Lancashire wicket-keeper.

SPECIAL NUMBERS

All these numbers have special significance for Lancashire. Can you say why?

981 25
982 £128,300
983 801
984 300*
985 173

RECENT MEMORY

986 Which Lancashire player toured the West Indies with the Under-19s in 1980?
987 In 1980 who hit his first Championship century against Derbyshire at Old Trafford?
988 Who bowled 13 consecutive maiden overs against Gloucestershire at Bristol in 1980?
989 Who sponsored the Floodlit Tournament in 1981?
990 On the England tour of the West Indies in 1981, which Lancashire player took 6 for 15 in the First Test?
991 Against which team did Lancashire score 408 for 6 in 1981?
992 In the Under-19s Test Match between England and India at Old Trafford, why was play stopped?
993 What milestone did Graeme Fowler pass at Southport in 1981 and what was special about it?
994 Who put on 213 for the fourth wicket against Somerset at Bath in 1984?
995 Who won the Gold Award in the semi-final of the Benson & Hedges Cup in 1984, but did not play in the final?
996 Who, on 20 July 1983, made his first appearance for Lancashire since 1976?
997 Who had a Testimonial for Lancashire in 1968 and another one for another County in 1984?
998 Who put on 115 for the last wicket in 1985 against Kent at Canterbury?

999 How many sixes did David Makinson hit in his 58* at Lytham in 1985?

1000 Who took 7 for 15 against Warwickshire at Southport in 1987?

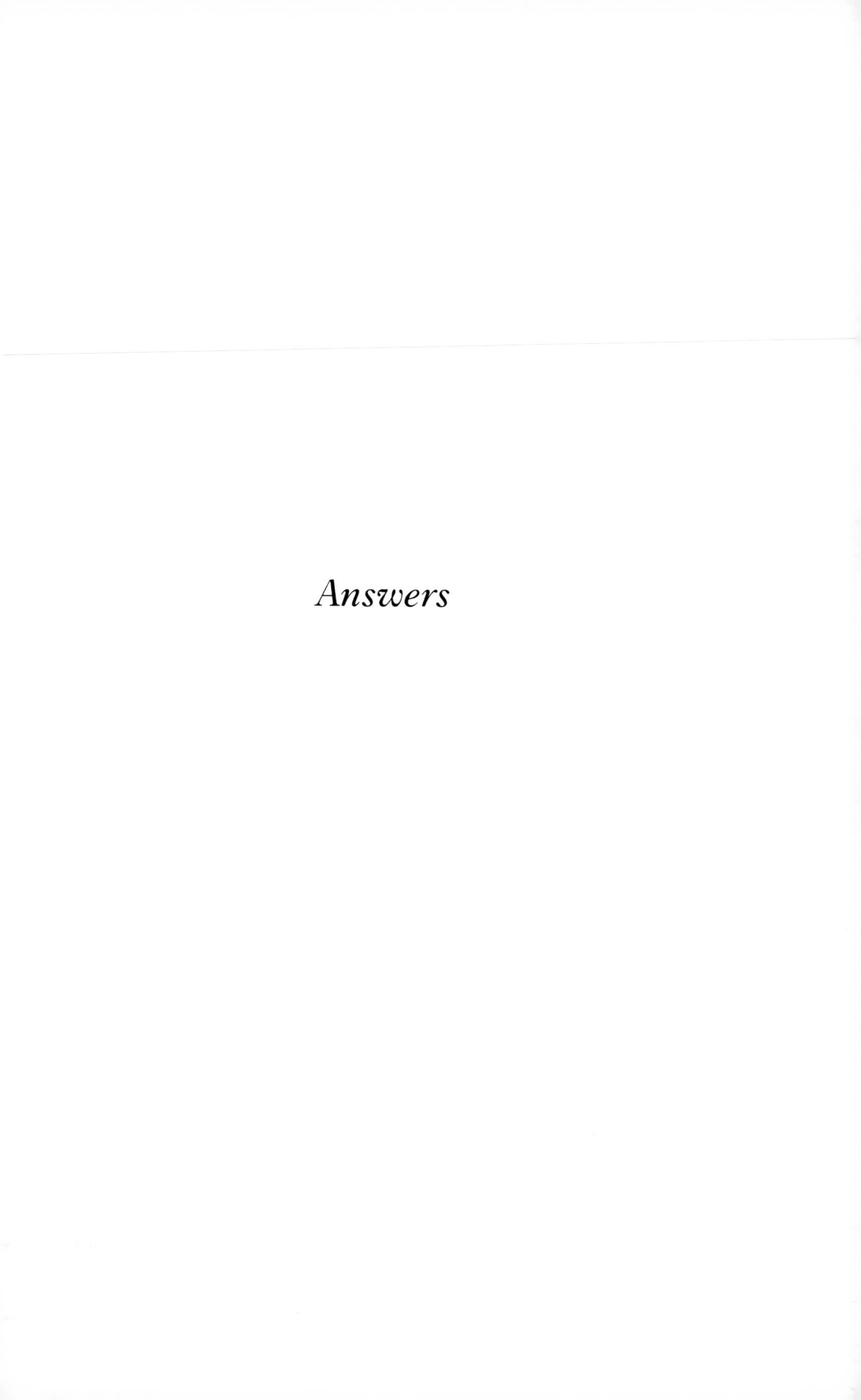

Answers

LANCASHIRE IN THE COUNTY CHAMPIONSHIP – 1

1 1926-27-28.
2 Derbyshire, in 1871 at Old Trafford.
3 801 v. Somerset at Taunton, 1895.
4 1950.
5 Surrey.
6 Somerset.
7 1952 v. Essex, Brentwood.
8 Leicestershire.
9 No.
10 1974. Won five, drew 15 (eighth).

LANCASHIRE IN THE COUNTY CHAMPIONSHIP – 2

11 1934.
12 P. Greenwood and M. Hilton.
13 J.T. Ikin.
14 Hampshire at Old Trafford.
15 Leonard Green.
16 Geoff Edrich, (1950-1951).
17 A. Appleby.
18 Derbyshire, in 1922 and 1923.
19 Bertie Buse.
20 Peter Lee in 1975.

OLD TRAFFORD

21 1865.
22 P. Lever, 1969 v. Notts.
23 F.B. Watson, 300* v. Surrey in 1928.
24 A.C. MacLaren, C. Washbrook, G. Duckworth, B. Statham.
25 Hornby (Road) and Barlow (Road).
26 Prince Philip, The Duke of Edinburgh.
27 A Red Cross hospital.
28 E.B. Rowley.

29 Fred Reynolds.
30 R.G. Barlow.

LANCASHIRE GROUNDS – AIGBURTH AND LIVERPOOL

31 1881, v. Cambridge University.
32 J.T. Tyldesley.
33 Nottinghamshire.
34 A.G. Steel.
35 Ted McDonald.
36 Cecil Parkin 1914.
37 Yorkshire.
38 Gordon Greenidge (Hampshire).
39 Glamorgan (1924).
40 West Indies.

LANCASHIRE GROUNDS – BLACKPOOL

41 K.J. Grieves, 202*.
42 W.J. Stewart (Warwickshire) in 1959.
43 1905, v. an England XI.
44 Victor Trumper.
45 Peter Eckersley.
46 Sussex.
47 D. Lloyd and F. Engineer.
48 Sir Lindsay Parkinson.
49 Bob Berry.
50 Worcestershire.

LANCASHIRE GROUNDS – SOUTHPORT

51 1959, v. Worcestershire.
52 J.B. Statham.
53 The Earl of Derby.

54 Glamorgan.
55 D. Lloyd, 116 and 104*.

LANCS v. WARWICKS, SOUTHPORT 1982

56 A. Kallicharran (234*) and G. Humpage (254).
57 Fourth.
58 D.J. Brown.
59 I. Cockbain, 98, and L.L. McFarlane, 6-59.
60 Ten.

OTHER LANCASHIRE GROUNDS

61 Lytham, 1985.
62 Yes, 1914, v. Warwickshire.
63 1935, v. Glamorgan.
64 Six – Blackpool, Lytham, Liverpool, Southport, Old Trafford, Preston (1952).
65 As a token of goodwill for allowing Lancashire to sign their professional, Australian Ted McDonald.

LANCASHIRE v. YORKSHIRE

66 None. 364 runs were scored.
67 King George V.
68 Gehan Mendis, 1987.
69 Whalley C.C.
70 30, at Holbeck in 1868.
71 G. Pullar.
72 Jack Simmons.
73 Clive Lloyd (6).
74 Chris Maynard.
75 C.H. Lloyd.

76 Roger Iddison.
77 R.H. Spooner, 200*.
78 A prisoner-of-war camp in Germany.
79 33.
80 R.G. Barlow, at Sheffield in 1871.
81 1885 – G.M. Kemp, 109 at Huddersfield.
82 1960.
83 Rev. J.R. Napier.
84 Walter Brearley.
85 Emmott Robinson.
86 F.H. Sugg, W. Robinson, E. Holgate and E. Rawlinson.
87 Len Hutton, 201.
88 A 100 partnership in each innings.
89 100 years of Roses cricket.
90 C. Hallows.

EARLY DAYS

91 Lancashire County and Manchester Cricket Club.
92 He alleged Lancashire played 'unfair bowlers'.
93 Middlesex, 1865.
94 A.N. Hornby and A. Appleby.
95 F.R. Spofforth.
96 1881.
97 R.G. Barlow.
98 R.G. Barlow, J. Briggs, A.G. Steel and R. Pilling.
99 A.N. Hornby.
100 J. Briggs.

1880-1900

101 A.N. Hornby, 1881.
102 A.W. Mold.
103 J. Briggs.
104 A.W. Mold and A. Ward.
105 T. Hayward, 315 for Surrey (Oval).
106 Father (J.A. MacLaren) – Treasurer. Son (A.C. MacLaren) – Captain.
107 F.H. Sugg.
108 Alfred Shaw.
109 A.C. MacLaren, v. Sussex at Brighton.
110 A.W. Mold.

1890s

111 A. Watson and J. Briggs.
112 A.G. Paul, 177.
113 A.W. Mold.
114 He took up a post at a Preparatory school.
115 J.Briggs and A.W. Mold.

A.C. MACLAREN'S 424

116 W.G. Grace. 344 had previously been the highest score in first-class cricket.
117 Sammy Woods.
118 A.G. Paul.
119 W. Ponsford – 429.
120 64 fours and one six.

THE GOLDEN AGE

121 Walter Brearley.
122 627, v. Notts., 601 for 8, v. Sussex.

123 Somerset.
124 J.J. Broughton.
125 Fred Reynolds.
126 The funeral of King Edward VII.
127 J.T. Tyldesley.
128 They were the first team to score over 400 runs to win a Championship game.
129 A bi-plane landed on the Ground.
130 Walter Brearley.

THE GOLDEN AGE – 1900s

131 Johnny Briggs.
132 Walter Brearley.
133 Harry Makepeace.
134 Yorkshire at Old Trafford.
135 K.S. Ranjitsinjhi.
136 Arthur Mold.
137 Sydney Barnes.
138 J. Phillips.
139 Ernest Tyldesley.
140 Walter Brearley.

AFTER THE FIRST WORLD WAR

141 Myles Kenyon.
142 Lancashire won by one run.
143 Richard Tyldesley.
144 Ernest Tyldesley.
145 Charles Hallows.
146 Hampshire.
147 Harry Makepeace, in 1923.
148 James Tyldesley.
149 Glamorgan at Cardiff.
150 W.R. Hammond and A.E. Dipper for Gloucestershire.

BETWEEN THE WARS – 1920s

151 J.T. Tyldesley.
152 R.G. Barlow.
153 H. Makepeace.
154 C. Hallows.
155 J.T. Tyldesley.

THREE CHAMPIONSHIPS IN THREE YEARS 1926

156 Ten.
157 Don Bradman.
158 Harry Makepeace and Ernest Tyldesley.
159 Ted McDonald.
160 Frank Woolley.

1927

161 Aigburth.
162 Nottinghamshire.
163 Wally Hammond.
164 E.A. McDonald.
165 Sussex.

1928

166 None.
167 F. Watson, 300*, and A. Sandham, 282*.
168 E. Tyldesley and F. Watson 371 for second wicket.
169 C. Hallows, H. Makepeace and E. Tyldesley.
170 Sydney Barnes.
171 Frank Watson.
172 George Duckworth.
173 107.

174 With it he completed 1,000 runs in May.
175 E. Tyldesley.

THE 1930s

176 E. Paynter and G. Duckworth.
177 1934-35.
178 Second.
179 Yorkshire.
180 Eddie Paynter.
181 Frank Sibbles.
182 He was the first to score 100 centuries in all first-class cricket and scored must runs in a career for Lancashire.
183 V.M. Merchant.
184 Gloucestershire.
185 Cyril Washbrook.
186 Tich Freeman.
187 H.R.W. Butterworth.
188 Jack Hobbs.
189 Peterborough.
190 Len Hopwood.
191 The Rest of England won.
192 Cyril Washbrook.
193 Frank Watson and Len Hopwood.
194 Arthur Wellard (Somerset).
195 Len Hopwood.

THE SECOND WORLD WAR AND AFTER

196 The Armed Forces.
197 Robert Menzies.
198 Cyril Washbrook.
199 German prisoners-of-war.
200 Widow and children of Hedley Verity.
201 C. Washbrook, W.B. Roberts, W.E. Phillipson and R. Pollard.

202 J.A. Fallows.
203 Jack Iddon.
204 T.E. Bailey, ten for 90 for Essex.
205 N.D. Howard.

CRICKET IN THE 1950s

206 He bowled two consecutive overs.
207 R. Berry.
208 Bertie Buse (Somerset).
209 T.E. Dickinson.
210 F.W. Moore.
211 Derbyshire and Cambridge University.
212 D.J. and C.S. Smith.
213 G. Clayton.
214 R. Tattersall.
215 R. Berry.
216 P.L. Winslow (South Africa).
217 F. Goodwin.
218 A. Wharton and J. Dyson.
219 G. Pullar.
220 P. Greenwood.
221 G.A. Edrich.
222 Surrey.
223 35 for eight.
224 W. Heys.
225 Geoff Pullar.

CRICKET IN THE 1960s

226 J.B. Statham (1951-1966).
227 I.M. Chappell.
228 G.K. Knox.
229 G. Pullar.
230 J.S. Savage.
231 D.S. Van Der Knapp.

232 Jack Bond.
233 J.B. Statham.
234 K. Higgs.
235 1963.
236 G. Pullar.
237 J.B. Statham.
238 J. Sullivan.
239 S. Ramadhin.
240 P. Marner and B.J. Booth.
241 K. Higgs.
242 K. Grieves.
243 G. Atkinson.
244 1969.
245 G. Pullar.

CRICKET IN THE 1970s

246 H. Pilling.
247 D. Lloyd.
248 R.M. Ratcliffe and J. Lyon.
249 P. Lee.
250 P.A. Robinson.
251 Four.
252 They finished 16th in the Championship table.
253 H. Pilling.
254 C.H. Lloyd.
255 F.C. Hayes.
256 J. Abrahams.
257 K. Shuttleworth.
258 A.K. James (Secretary).
259 B. Wood and D. Lloyd scored 299.
260 J. Cumbes.
261 D.P. Hughes.
262 K. Shutleworth and P. Lever.
263 Barry Wood in 1979.
264 Frank Hayes.
265 David Lloyd.

THE 1980s

266 Six.
267 He became the first Lancashire player to take a hat-trick and score a 50 in the same match.
268 Nasir Zaidi.
269 Barry Wood (then with Derbyshire).
270 Soren Henriksen.
271 It was the first time a team had won 24-0 under the present points system.
272 John Abrahams and Graeme Fowler.
273 I. Folley, B.P. Patterson and M. Watkinson.
274 G. Fowler and A.N. Hayhurst.
275 K.W. McLeod.
276 Trevor Jesty.
277 G. Fowler, P. Allott and G.D. Mendis all attended Durham University.
278 Graham Lloyd.
279 Glen Turner for Worcestershire.
280 Cambridge University.
281 Graeme Fowler.
282 Frank Hayes.
283 David Hughes.
284 I. Cockbain, D.W. Varey, A.J. Murphy and B. Wood
285 Northampton.

CAPTAINS

286 G.R. Bardswell.
287 Ken Cranston, 1947-48.
288 Surrey and Lancashire shared the County Championship in 1950 and they both captained their sides.
289 J.F. Blackledge and J. Fallows.
290 P.T. Eckersley.
291 Leonard Green, 1926, 1927, 1928.
292 Ken Cranston, Nigel Howard, Cyril Washbrook, Bob Barber, Joe Blackledge, Ken Grieves.

293 E.B. Rowley.
294 President.
295 Cyril Washbrook in 1954.

LANCASHIRE PLAYERS

296 G.E. Tyldesley, 573; J. Sharp, 518; J.T. Tyldesley, 507; C. Washbrook, 500.
297 Roy Tattersall.
298 N. Oldfield (1935) and K. Cranston (1948).
299 Len Hopwood.
300 Nigel Howard.
301 Fred Reynolds in 1870.
302 Jack Sharp.
303 Roy Tattersall (171 wickets, 1950).
304 14 were bowled, one was lbw.
305 Both wicket-keepers were chosen – G. Duckworth and W. Farrimond.

PREVIOUS ADDRESSES

306 Norman Oldfield.
307 Alan Wharton.
308 Sydney Barnes.
309 Ian Cockbain.
310 Ian Chappell.
311 Charles Edward de Trafford.
312 David Van Der Knapp.
313 Jim Cumbes (four).
314 Steve Jefferies.
315 C.R. Hartley.
316 Gehan Mendis scored 103 and 100* for Sussex at Hastings in 1985.
317 Cec Parkin.
318 Alan Wharton, Brian Booth, Peter Marner, Ken Higgs, Ken Shuttleworth, John Savage.

319 Jim Hilton, Geoff Clayton, Geoff Lomax, Graham Atkinson, Tom Dickinson.
320 P.A. Robinson, Steve Jefferies, John Abrahams, D.S. Van Der Knapp.

MISSING NAMES

321 Campbell.
322 Makepeace.
323 Farokh Engineer.
324 Gorton.
325 Walter.
326 Francis.
327 Croft.
328 Eckersley.
329 Greenhalgh.
330 Neilson.
331 Granville.
332 McFarlane.
333 Walcott.
334 Thomas.
335 Poidevin.
336 Wilfred.
337 Royle.
338 Herbert.
339 Darbyshire.
340 Litton.

JACK SIMMONS

341 Nottinghamshire at Liverpool in 1977.
342 First player to receive a benefit of over £100,000.
343 John Derrick (Glamorgan).
344 Always likes to be last on the field.
345 Old Trafford v. Worcestershire.

ERNEST TYLDESLEY

346 1912.
347 Northants at Peterborough.
348 45.
349 3,024.
350 1936.

NICKNAMES

351 Harry Makepeace.
352 Alan Wilson.
353 Jack Dyson.
354 Barry Wood.
355 Brian Statham.
356 Frank Hayes.
357 John Ikin.
358 A.N. Hornby.
359 Clive Lloyd.
360 Norman Oldfield.
361 Jack Latchford.
362 Peter Lever.
363 Geoff Clayton.
364 Peter Lee.
365 Harry Pilling.
366 David Lloyd.
367 Keith Goodwin.
368 Lawrence Cook.
369 John Abrahams.
370 Ian Folley.

YOUNGEST/OLDEST

371 Roy Tattersall in 1950.
372 M.A. Atherton in 1987.
373 P.T. Marner – 16 years and five months.

374 A.N. Hornby – 52 years and five months.
375 33, between 1867 and 1899 (record).
376 A.C. MacLaren (1894) 22 years and 160 days.
377 Cyril Washbrook.
378 G. Pullar in (1959, aged 24).
379 Harry Makepeace (in 1929, aged 47).
380 A.N. Hornby (in 1898, aged 51 and in 1899 for three games, aged 52).

RELATIVELY SPEAKING

381 (c) John scored 31,949, Ernest scored 34,222.
382 D.W. Varey, bowled by J.G. Varey at Lord's in 1982.
383 Each scored centuries in the same innings in consecutive matches.
384 Bill (Middlesex), Brian (Kent and Glamorgan).
385 Lance Gibbs.
386 Steel – D.Q., E.E., A.G., and H.B.
387 Colin, Jim and Malcolm (Colin not related).
388 Barry, Kenneth, Nigel and Rupert.
389 Barry and Nigel were brothers, sons of Rupert.
390 G.A. and E.H. Edrich, B.J. and N.D. Howard, M.J. and J. Hilton, D.J. and C.S. Smith.

CYRIL WASHBROOK

391 Eight.
392 E. Tyldesley,in 1926.
393 He scored a double century against Yorkshire Second XI.
394 76.
395 Headingley.

A.C. MACLAREN

396 His wife's health needed a warmer climate.
397 Harrow.
398 They presented him with a gold watch and life membership.
399 W.G. Grace.
400 200 not out for M.C.C. v. New Zealand XI.

JOHNNY BRIGGS

401 16.
402 Widnes.
403 He made a century and took a hat-trick.
404 He and Pilling put on 173 for the last wicket.
405 Cheadle Asylum.

BRIAN STATHAM

406 1816, (average 15.12) betwen 1950 and 1968.
407 62, v. Leicestershire, 1955.
408 The Australian Tourists.
409 252.
410 Yorkshire at Old Trafford in 1968.

CLIVE LLOYD

411 110.
412 Warwickshire.
413 Six.
414 Glamorgan at Swansea.
415 1975.

DAVID HUGHES

416 Newton-Le-Willows.
417 24.
418 B.S. Bedi.
419 Tasmania.
420 1970.

EDDIE PAYNTER

421 Hove v. Sussex.
422 Age 29, v. Warwickshire at Old Trafford in 1931.
423 Lost the top of two fingers in an accident.
424 He kept wicket when Ames broke a finger. He also scored 99 and 43.
425 Trent Bridge, 216* v. Australia, 1938; Durban, 243 v. South Africa, 1938-39.

GEORGE DUCKWORTH

426 Warwickshire.
427 1924.
428 1,090 – 751 caught and 339 stumped.
429 Rugby League.
430 1928 – 28 stumped, 69 caught.

WHO WAS HE?

431 Barry Wood.
432 Alan Wharton.
433 Trevor Jesty.
434 Ken Cranston in 1947.
435 David Lloyd.
436 J.T. Tyldesley, 1897-1919.
437 Johnny Briggs, 1887-1900.

438 J.L. Hopwood.
439 R.G. Barlow in Layton cemetery, Blackpool.
440 G.M. Taylor, 1924 to 1980.
441 A.N. Hornby.
442 R.G. Barlow.
443 Jack Sharp.
444 C. Washbrook and J.T. Tyldesley.
445 Harry Makepeace.
446 J.B. Statham.
447 Arthur Booth.
448 K. Higgs, 128 with John Snow.
449 F.D. Parr.
450 Alan Wilson.
451 Albert Ward.
452 Harry Dean.
453 Lol Cook.
454 Dick Pollard.
455 Eddie Paynter.
456 R.A. Boddington.
457 Gordon Hodgson.
458 Fred Reynolds.
459 Oswald Lancashire.
460 Roy Tattersall.
461 Andrew Kennedy.
462 Roy Tattersall.
463 Alan Wharton.
464 Lionel Lister.
465 Len Wilkinson.
466 Eddie Phillipson.
467 Cyril Washbrook.
468 E.A. McDonald.
469 Ken Grieves.
470 Geoff Edrich. Middlesex were captained by Bill Edrich.

BIRTHPLACES

471 Cecil Parkin.
472 R.G. Barlow.
473 Neal Radford.
474 Cyril Washbrook.
475 Patrick Patterson.
476 G.K. Knox.
477 John Abrahams.
478 Ken Cranston.
479 J.Briggs and J.Crossland.
480 G.A. Edrich.
481 Ken Higgs.
482 A.J. Good.
483 D.M. Green.
484 K.J. Grieves.
485 Kevin Hayes.
486 Trevor Jesty.
487 Clive Lloyd.
488 Harry Makepeace.
489 Gehan Mendis.
490 R.H. Spooner.

BENEFITS

491 G.R. Baker.
492 A. Mold in 1900.
493 W. Cuttell and C. Smith in 1903.
494 R.H. Spooner, 200*.
495 Frank Sibbles in 1937.
496 Lord Hawke.
497 William Mycroft.
498 The match for Geoff Pullar in 1967.
499 Ken Shuttleworth and John Sullivan.
500 Cyril Washbrook, Ernest Tyldesley, Clive Lloyd, Brian Statham.

OPENERS

501 Five* – R.G. Barlow.
502 There were no centuries. His highest score was 85.
503 B.J. Booth and K. Tebay, v. Worcestershire, Old Trafford.
504 Glamorgan, at Swansea.
505 1963 v. Derbyshire at Liverpool by B.J. Booth.
506 D.M. Green, v. Glamorgan, Cardiff, 1964.
507 W. Place.
508 R.G. Barlow (11).
509 G. Pullar and B.J. Booth.
510 P. Holmes and H. Sutcliffe for Yorkshire, 323 (1931) and 253 (1919).

GREAT BATTING

511 Charles Hallows.
512 1928.
513 J.T. Tyldesey in 1901.
514 A.N. Hornby in 1881.
515 E. Tyldesley, J.T. Tyldesley, C. Washbrook, H. Makepeace, F. Watson, J. Sharp, J. Iddon, K.J. Grieves, C. Hallows.
516 Both scored 1,000 runs in July.
517 J.D. Bond scored 2,112 in 1962.
518 W. Place scored 266 v. Oxford University, C. Washbrook scored 251* v. Surrey, both in 1947.
519 R. Subba Row scored 260* for Northants in 1955, G.E. Humpage scored 254 for Warwickshire in 1982.
520 J.T. Tyldesley (13).

CENTURIES

521 E. Tyldesley in 1928.
522 Jack Sharp at the Oval.
523 Tom Hayward (Surrey), Dennis Amiss (Warwickshire).
524 J. Ricketts, A.C. MacLaren, R. Whitehead.

525 He had a runner in both innings because of injury.
526 E. Tyldesley.
527 1926 and 1928.
528 Graeme Fowler.
529 A.H. Hornby. 100 in 43 minutes v. Somerset.
530 Harry Pilling in 1970, v. Warwickshire.
531 J. Iddon and E. Tyldesley.
532 Mark Chadwick and Kevin Hayes.
533 Winston Place.
534 R.H. Spooner and A.C. MacLaren in 1904.
535 R. Iddison, who scored 106 v. Surrey 1866.
536 Rev. F.W. Wright scored 120* v. Sussex in 1869.
537 A.C. MacLaren.
538 J.T. Tyldesley.
539 R.H. Spooner.
540 J.A. Ormrod (Worcestershire).

DOUBLE CENTURIES AND MORE

541 J. Abrahams.
542 Eddie Paynter, who scored 322 v. Sussex at Hove.
543 Cyril Washbrook.
544 Clive Lloyd, v. Warwickshire, 217*.
545 Old Trafford.
546 G. Fowler and John Abrahams.
547 Frank Watson in 1928.
548 248 by J.T. Tyldesley 1903; 264 W.R. Hammond for Gloucestershire 1932.
549 E. Paynter, 322; F. Watson, 300*; and A.C. MacLaren, 424*.
550 G. Mendis scored 203* v. Middlesex in 1987.

NOTABLE PARTNERSHIPS

551 David Varey and Harry Pilling.
552 J. Briggs and R. Pilling, v. Surrey 1885.
553 Fastest double century partnership in first-class cricket, v. Leicestershire, at Old Trafford in 1983 – 43 minutes.
554 Liverpool.
555 Gloucestershire.
556 J. Lyon.
557 A. Needham and R.D. Jackman.
558 Andrew Kennedy.
559 Fifth.
560 L.O.S. Poidevin and A. Kermode.

FIELDING AND WICKET-KEEPING

561 Richard Pilling.
562 M.L. Taylor.
563 G. Fowler, v. Pakistan, 1983-84.
564 K. Grieves.
565 1950 and 1953.
566 Rev. Vernon Royle.
567 R.K. Tyldesley and K. Grieves.
568 G. Duckworth (922), R. Pilling (486), F.M. Engineer (464).
569 W. Farrimond (7), v. Kent (Old Trafford), 1930.
570 G. Clayton (1959) and C. Maynard (1982) – nine.

GREAT BOWLING

571 Harry Dean.
572 Walter Brearley.
573 Johnny Briggs.
574 Sydney Barnes and Walter Brearley.
575 Johnny Briggs.
576 Bob Berry v. Worcestershire (Blackpool), 1953.
577 Brian Statham 1,816.

578 J.T. Ikin.
579 R.G. Barlow.
580 Johnny Briggs, v. Sussex 1897.
581 Harry Dean.
582 Brian Statham (2,260) and Johnny Briggs (2,221).
583 Brian Statham.
584 Roy Tattersall, v. Notts, 1953.
585 H. Dean and W. Brearley.
586 E.A. McDonald in 1925.
587 198.
588 R.G. Barlow and E.A. McDonald.
589 A. Mold.
590 Johnny Briggs.
591 Wasim Akram, v. Surrey, Southport, 1988.
592 S.T. Jefferies. Eight for 46 v. Notts, Trent Bridge, 1983.
593 He took all 10 Lancashire wickets in an innings.
594 Brian Statham, Ken Higgs, Tommy Greenhough.
595 Harry Dean.
596 Arthur Mold and Cec Parkin.
597 John Crossland.
598 W.R. Cuttell in 1898.
599 Yorkshire.
600 Jack Hallows.

THE TORTOISE AND THE HARE

601 R.H. Spooner.
602 Jack Simmons.
603 34, (six, four, six, six, six, six).
604 35 minutes.
605 David Gower.
606 25.
607 A.H. Hornby.
608 Leicestershire, at Old Trafford in 1983.
609 A.N. Hornby.
610 B.P. King.

DEBUTS

611 Ralph Whitehead.
612 Frank Woolley.
613 A.C. MacLaren.
614 Brian Statham.
615 Norman Oldfield in 1935.
616 Michael Atherton in 1987 (Cambridge University and Lancashire).
617 J.J. Broughton.
618 94.
619 S.F. Barnes at 38 years and 240 days.
620 Geoff Lawson.

LANCASHIRE PLAYERS IN TEST CRICKET

621 Johnny Briggs
622 Ken Higgs.
623 Christchurch in 1951 – W.D. Hadlee, New Zealand captain, recalled him.
624 J.B. Statham – 70.
625 George Duckworth.
626 G. Fowler.
627 A.N. Hornby, A.G. Steel, A.C.MacLaren, K. Cranston and N.D. Howard.
628 Peter Lever and Ken Shuttleworth.
629 N. Oldfield.
630 Eddie Paynter.
631 R.G. Barlow.
632 Johnny Briggs, eight for 11 v. South Africa, 1889.
633 Geoff Pullar, v. West Indies Port of Spain, 1959-60.
634 Sydney Barnes, 49 v. South Africa.
635 Ken Cranston.
636 Johnny Briggs.
637 Jack Sharp.
638 Dick Tyldesley.
639 G. Duckworth and W. Farrimond both kept wicket in Test matches.

640 C. Washbrook, A. Wharton, J.B. Statham, J.T. Ikin, N.D. Howard, R. Berry, W. Place, M.J. Hilton, R. Tattersall.

TEST DEBUTS

641 Pat Patterson, West Indies v. England, Kingston, 1986.
642 W.E. Phillipson.
643 Ken Cranston.
644 J.H. Makepeace (aged 39).
645 Ken Cranston.
646 Dick Pollard.
647 At Headingley against Pakistan, 1982.
648 R. Pollard 1946, P. Allott 1981, K. Cranston 1947 and N.H. Fairbrother 1987.
649 A.N. Hornby in 1879.
650 Brian Statham and Ken Cranston.

LAKER'S TEST MATCH 1956

651 Tony Lock.
652 Stretford end.
653 Jim Burke.
654 Peter Richardson and Rev. David Sheppard.
655 Alan Oakman.
656 Frizinghall, Yorkshire.
657 Neil Harvey and Ken Mackay.
658 C.C. McDonald.
659 J.B. Statham and C. Washbrook.
660 He took ten for 88 against the Australians.

TEST CRICKET AT OLD TRAFFORD

661 K.S. Ranjitsinjhi in 1896.
662 Extras were the main contributor to England's second innings and to their match aggregate (unique at Test level).

663 Ian Craig (Australia, 1956).
664 Paul Terry.
665 Clive Lloyd.
666 1902 – Fred Tate's match.
667 The youngest player to play Test cricket for England.
668 C. Hunte and G. Sobers.
669 L.Gibbs.
670 Seven (seven for 22).
671 Ray Illingworth.
672 Peter Lever – 88 not out.
673 A.A. Lilley (England), 1896, and C.L. Walcott (West Indies), 1950.
674 Gordon Greenidge – 134 and 101.
675 Abbas Ali Baig.
676 W.M. Lawry scored 106.
677 T.R. Veivers.
678 Highest score by an England player at Old Trafford.
679 South Africa.
680 T.W. Graveney.
681 R.G. Willis.
682 G.O. B. Allen (3w – four no-balls).
683 Tom Cartwright.
684 Warwick Armstrong in 1921.
685 Tony Lock – Jim Laker took 19 for 90.
686 T.J. Mathews, Australia, v. South Africa, Old Trafford, 1912.
687 71 in 1976 and 93 in 1988.
688 Tim Robinson.
689 India, 58 and 82, 1952.
690 Conrad Hunte.

ONE – DAY INTERNATIONALS AT OLD TRAFFORD

691 Canada in 1979.
692 Bill Athey.
693 India.

694 1972 v. Australia.
695 D.L. Amiss 103 not out.
696 Glenn Turner 114 not out.
697 Pakistan.
698 M.A. Holding.
699 First batsman to score 3,000 runs in one-day internationals.
700 Alan Lamb.

CRICKET AND FOOTBALL

701 Everton.
702 Jack Sharp and Harry Makepeace.
703 Jack Dyson.
704 Jim Cumbes.
705 Ken Higgs.
706 Peter Greenwood.
707 Fred Goodwin.
708 R.G. Barlow.
709 Jim Cumbes.
710 Frank Sugg.

CRICKET AND OTHER SPORTS

711 Alan Wharton.
712 Rugby Union.
713 Graham Atkinson.
714 Huddersfield and Wigan.
715 Bob Barber.
716 R.G. Barlow.
717 A.N. Hornby.
718 Leonard Green.
719 A.G. Paul.
720 William Barron.

OTHERWISE OCCUPIED – 1

721 William Findlay
722 A.G. Steel.
723 Dick Pollard.
724 S.H. Swire and R. Howard.
725 Rev. V. Royle, Rev. J.R. Napier, Rev F.W. Wright.
726 Rupert Howard.
727 G.M. Kemp.
728 Graeme Fowler.
729 L.O.S. Poidevin.
730 Harry Pilling.

OTHERWISE OCCUPIED – 2

731 Ken Cranston.
732 Five.
733 P.T. Eckersley, F. Hardcastle, Sir George Kemp, Sir Joseph Leese, Sir Lancelot Sanderson.
734 J.M. Tindall.
735 Eddie Phillipson.
736 Jack Sharp.
737 Cec Parkin.
738 Alan Wharton.
739 Geoff Edrich.
740 P.T. Eckersley.

BOOK TITLES

741 John Kay.
742 Michael Down.
743 R.G. Barlow.
744 Eddie Paynter.
745 George Brooking.
746 W.E. Howard.
747 T.R.F. Prittie.

748 Brian Statham.
749 A.C. MacLaren.
750 Neville Cardus.
751 Ron Yeomans.
752 Clive Lloyd.
753 Jack Simmons with Brian Bearshaw.
754 Cecil Parkin.
755 John Marshall.
756 A.A. Thomson.
757 Cyril Washbrook.
758 Brian Statham.
759 Cyril Washbrook.
760 Vernon Addison and Brian Bearshaw.

QUOTES AND AUTHORS

761 Neville Cardus on C.G. McCartney.
762 A.C. MacLaren.
763 R.G. Barlow talking about A.N. Hornby.
764 Eddie Paynter.
765 They all wrote a cricket book called *Close of Play*.

NEVILLE CARDUS AND LANCASHIRE

766 A.C. MacLaren.
767 R.H. Spooner.
768 L.L. Wilkinson.
769 Cec Parkin.
770 Ernest Tyldesley.
771 Sydney Barnes.
772 Cyril Washbrook.
773 Walter Brearley.
774 Harry Makepeace.
775 Johnny Briggs.

TRUE OR FALSE?

776 True.
777 False.
778 True.
779 True.
780 True.
781 False.
782 False.
783 False.
784 True.
785 True.

TRUE OR FALSE? –2

786 True – Women's Test, 1937.
787 True – A.E. Hall.
788 True.
789 False – 990.
790 True.
791 True (Ladies' lacrosse).
792 False.
793 False – It was the First World War.
794 True – Bill Lawton, 1948.
795 False – He scored 98.

ANAGRAMS

796 Alec Watson.
797 Roy Tattersall.
798 Graeme Fowler.
799 Frank Hayes.
800 Clive Lloyd.
801 Cec Parkin.
802 Barry Wood.
803 Gehan Mendis.

804 David Green.
805 Alan Bolton.
806 Keith Goodwin.
807 Barry Howard.
808 Leonard Green.
809 Leslie Warburton.
810 Roger Iddison.
811 Frank Watson.
812 Bernard Reidy.
813 Ken Cranston.
814 Peter Lee.
815 Bill Roberts.

ONE-DAY MATCHES

816 D. Lloyd and C.H. Lloyd.
817 Double – John Player League and Gillette Cup.
818 Lambert and Butler floodlit competition.
819 Mike Watkinson.
820 Three Gillette Cup finals, two John Player Trophy.
821 John Abrahams.
822 Scotland in 1986.
823 They used orange balls.
824 The Ward Knock-Out competition.
825 Paul Allott (semi-final), Mike Watkinson (final).

NATWEST/GILLETTE CUP

826 P. Marner, 121 v. Leicester, 1963.
827 S.P. Davis for Durham.
828 Clive and David Lloyd, v. Gloucestershire, 1978.
829 Gloucestershire.
830 Jack Simmons.
831 131* – A. Kennedy, v. Middlesex, 1978.
832 Worcestershire.
833 None.

834 78 – P. Lever.
835 C. Lloyd, 1,920, D. Lloyd, 1,207, B. Wood, 1,236.
836 Eight.
837 No one.
838 Five.
839 Graeme Fowler.
840 65.

LANCASHIRE v. GLOUCESTERSHIRE SEMI-FINAL 1971

841 Mike Procter.
842 Jack Bond.
843 Four, six, two, two, four, six.
844 Barry Wood.
845 Ten minutes to nine.

SEVEN GILLETTE/NATWEST CUP FINALS AT LORD'S

846 Harry Pilling.
847 John Abrahams.
848 Sussex.
849 Jack Bond's catch off Asif Iqbal.
850 Warwickshire.
851 No.
852 A. Kennedy.
853 Northants.
854 Neil Fairbrother.
855 D.A. Reeve (Sussex).

JOHN PLAYER/REFUGE ASSURANCE SUNDAY LEAGUE

856 N.H. Fairbrother and G. Fowler in 1987 v. Somerset.
857 1969, 1970.
858 Harry Pilling – 625 in 1970.

859 Clive Lloyd.
860 C.D. Matthews v. Worcestershire, at Old Trafford in 1988.
861 Ken Shuttleworth, J. Simmons, D.P. Hughes.
862 A. Worsick and D.K. Beckett.
863 S.J. O'Shaughnessy.
864 Harry Pilling in 1970.
865 Southport, Liverpool, Blackpool, Old Trafford.
866 Jack Simmons.
867 K.M. Krikken (his father was B.E. Krikken).
868 J. Simmons, 1970, K. Higgs, 1969, and D.P. Hughes, 1976.
869 Jim Cumbes: Lancashire, Surrey, Worcestershire, Warwickshire.
870 Essex, 75 in 1984; Lancashire, 71 in 1987.
871 D. Lloyd, 4,653 and C. Lloyd, 5,198.
872 Jack Simmons (289).
873 David Lloyd (76).
874 F. Engineer, 116 – 95 catches and 21 stumpings.
875 D.P. Hughes (84).

BENSON & HEDGES CUP

876 D. Lloyd and B. Reidy.
877 Peter May.
878 K. Higgs for Leicestershire.
879 Barry Wood (ten).
880 Yorkshire.
881 D. Lloyd and F.C. Hayes.
882 Colin Croft, 6 for 10.
883 Mark Chadwick.
884 Glamorgan.
885 Worcestershire.

ODDS AND ENDS

886 Colonel.
887 Tewkesbury, Gloucestershire.

888 Norman Oldfield and Harry Pilling.
889 Cec Parkin and Lol Cook.
890 Geoff Edrich.
891 Jim Cumbes.
892 Roy Collins.
893 Colin Everton Hunte Croft.
894 Neil Harvey Fairbrother.
895 Charles Oliver.
896 At Aigburth in 1880, when O.P. Lancashire played for Cambridge University against Lancashire.
897 The Barton Arcade.
898 D. Lloyd (England), I.M. Chappell (Australia), F.M. Engineer (India), C.H. Lloyd (West Indies).
899 He suffered an accident whilst hunting.
900 C. Washbrook and J.D. Bond.
901 1924.
902 Parsee.
903 Len Hopwood and Cyril Washbrook.
904 Eddie Phillipson.
905 Richard Hadlee.
906 Aigburth, Liverpool.
907 Jack Iddon – at Old Trafford, Liverpool, Blackpool, Preston and Blackburn.
908 A. Ward, F.H. Sugg, C. Smith, W.R. Cuttell, G.R. Baker, J. I'Anson.
909 Malcolm Hilton.
910 Yorkshire.
911 Harry Pilling.
912 Geoff Edrich.
913 W.R. Hammond with 65.
914 Yes.
915 Carphone Captain of the year.

CURIOUS

916 David Lloyd – 1978.
917 Jack Simmons, with Tasmania and Lancashire.

918 John Arlott.
919 Arthur Wrigley.
920 Peter Eckersley.
921 Tom Reddick.
922 W.B. Roberts.
923 H. Rylance.
924 R.K., W.K., J.D., and H.
925 D.W . Varey.

TWENTY QUESTIONS

926 J. I'Anson.
927 F.S. Booth.
928 S.F. Barnes.
929 A.J. Birtwell.
930 Associated Tyre Specialists.
931 James MacLaren and J.C. Fallows.
932 R. Pollard and L.L. Wilkinson.
933 The Earl of Derby.
934 Alec Douglas Home and Harold Wilson.
935 J.S. Cragg 1965-66 and 1968.
936 Rev. Vernon Royle and Canon F. Paton Williams.
937 Eight – J.D. Bond, J. Bowes, D. Lloyd, N. Oldfield, W.E. Phillipson, E. Paynter, W. Place and H. Elliott.
938 Three – W.E. Phillipson, N. Oldfield and H. Elliott.
939 Five – H. Williams, H.C. Flack, G. Prosser, C. Hawkins and P. Marron.
940 A.K. James.
941 C. Washbrook and W. Place. (Record 368 for the first wicket A.C. MacLaren and R.H. Spooner.)
942 150 by A. Ward and C.R. Hartley, v. Leicestershire in 1900.
943 G.M. Taylor in 1965.
944 Nottinghamshire, 202 times.
945 England v. Australia in 1961.

WHOSE AUTOGRAPH?

946 Tommy Greenhough.
947 Frank Hayes.
948 L.O.S. Poidevin.
949 Geoff Pullar.
950 Patrick Patterson.
951 D.R. Worsley.
952 Ian Folley.
953 Ken Cranston.
954 Ian Austin.
955 Peter Lever.
956 Chris Maynard.
957 Gehan Mendis.
958 David Varey.
959 Soren Henrikson.
960 Warren Hegg.
961 Geoff Clayton.
962 David Lloyd.
963 Colin Hilton.
964 Mark Chadwick.
965 Alan Ormrod.

WORD SEARCH

A	S	H	N	O	C	P	L	W	T
L	E	M	I	N	O	R	Y	A	L
S	T	E	C	L	R	E	O	N	Y
E	R	N	A	L	T	W	D	F	A
T	A	D	N	O	E	O	L	I	T
R	L	I	S	Y	C	E	N	T	R
E	D	S	I	D	W	L	B	T	I
I	E	K	M	R	C	O	N	O	S
D	R	I	M	I	N	T	O	L	W
L	S	N	L	D	T	E	R	D	E

LAST SEASON

966 P.J. Defreitas and Ronnie Irani.
967 Six.
968 N.H. Fairbrother (first-class, Benson & Hedges and Refuge)
969 Gordon Garlick.
970 None.
971 Graeme Fowler.
972 Graham Hick, 212 for Worcestershire at Old Trafford.
973 G.D. Lloyd, C.D. Mathews, T.E. Jesty and Wasim Akram.
974 Neil Fairbrother 106.
975 N.H. Fairbrother (April/May), G.D. Mendis (June), Wasim Akram (July), P.J.W. Allott (Aug/Sept).
976 Little Lever.
977 Paul Allott.
978 M.A. Atherton.
979 Manchester Grammar School.
980 A tramp asleep.

SPECIALNUMBERS

981 Lancashire's lowest score v. Derbyshire, Old Trafford, 1871.
982 Lancashire's record Benefit for Jack Simmons.
983 Lancashire's highest score v. Somerset at Taunton, 1895.
984 The highest individual score for Lancashire at Old Trafford, F. Watson v. Surrey, 1928.
985 The record last-wicket partnership for Lancashire, J. Briggs and R. Pilling v. Surrey, Liverpool, 1885.

RECENT MEMORY

986 Steven O'Shaughnessy.
987 Andrew Kennedy 169*.
988 David Hughes.
989 Lambert & Butler.
990 Colin Croft.
991 Derbyshire.
992 The sun was shining in the players' eyes.
993 He passed his 1,000 runs for the season and was the first uncapped player to do so since 1964.
994 Steven O'Shaughnessy and David Hughes.
995 Mark Chadwick.
996 Peter Lever in the NatWest Trophy Match against Somerset at Old Trafford.
997 Ken Higgs – his second testimonial was with Leicestershire.
998 Paul Allott and John Stanworth.
999 Seven.
1000 Ian Folley.

PICTURE QUIZ

1 Johnnie Briggs.
2 Cyril Washbrook.
3 Dick Pollard.
4 1948 Test Match. Johnson catches a ball on the Pavilion balcony.
5 Yorkshire.
6 1960.
7 Middlesex.
8 Heys, Jordan, Wilson and Clayton.
9 S.F. Barnes.
10 M.F. Malone.
11 Jack Simmons.
12 Steve O'Shaughnessy.
13 Simmons, Sullivan, Shuttleworth, Snellgrove, Pilling, Bond, D. Lloyd, Bailey, Wood, Hayes, Lever, Hughes and Savage 1970.

14 Paul Allott.
15 Middlesex.
16 Farokh Engineer.
17 Alex Mortimer conducting Pilling, Simmons, Savage, Bond, D. Lloyd and Atkinson.
18 Alf Barlow.
19 Paul Allott and Dennis Lillee.
20 Barry Wood and Bob Taylor.
21 Rev. Vernon Royle.
22 W. Farrimond.
23 Jack Iddon.
24 Jack Ikin.
25 Walter Brearley and Archie MacLaren.
26 Winston Place.
27 Tommy Greenhough.
28 N.D. Howard.